Bouvard and Pécuchet

A TRAGI-COMIC NOVEL OF BOURGEOIS LIFE

BY

GUSTAVE FLAUBERT

———

VOLUME X.

SIMON P. MAGEE
PUBLISHER
CHICAGO, ILL.

CONTENTS

BOUVARD AND PÉCUCHET

(*Continued.*)

(vii)

ILLUSTRATIONS

BOUVARD AND PÉCUCHET

(CONTINUED.)

CHAPTER IX.

SONS OF THE CHURCH.

ARCEL reappeared next day at three
o'clock, his face green, his eyes
bloodshot, a lump on his forehead,
his breeches torn, his breath tainted
with a strong smell of brandy, and
his person covered with dirt.

He had been, according to an annual custom of
his, six leagues away at Iqueville to enjoy a midnight
repast with a friend; and, stuttering more than ever,
crying, wishing to beat himself, he begged of them
for pardon, as if he had committed a crime. His
masters granted it to him. A singular feeling of se-
renity rendered them indulgent.

The snow had suddenly melted, and they walked
about the garden, inhaling the genial air, delighted
merely with living.

Was it only chance that had kept them from
death? Bouvard felt deeply affected. Pécuchet re-

called his first commission, and, full of gratitude to the Force, the Cause, on which they depended, the idea took possession of them to read pious works.

The Gospel dilated their souls, dazzled them like a sun. They perceived Jesus standing on a mountain, with one arm raised, while below the multitude listened to Him; or else on the margin of a lake in the midst of the apostles, while they drew in their nets; next on the ass, in the clamour of the "alleluias," His hair fanned by the quivering palms; finally, lifted high upon the Cross, bending down His head, from which eternally falls a dew of blood upon the world. What won them, what ravished them, was His tenderness for the humble, His defence of the poor, His exaltation of the oppressed; and they found in that Book, wherein Heaven unfolds itself, nothing theological in the midst of so many precepts, no dogma, no requirement, save purity of heart.

As for the miracles, their reason was not astonished by them. They had been acquainted with them from their childhood. The loftiness of St. John enchanted Pécuchet, and better disposed him to appreciate the *Imitation*.

Here were no more parables, flowers, birds, but lamentations — a compression of the soul into itself.

Bouvard grew sad as he turned over these pages, which seemed to have been written in foggy weather, in the depths of a cloister, between a belfry and a tomb. Our mortal life appeared there so wretched that one must needs forget it and return to God. And the two poor men, after all their disappointments, experienced that need of simple natures — to love something, to find rest for their souls.

They studied *Ecclesiastes, Isaiah, Jeremiah.*

But the Bible dismayed them with its lion-voiced prophets, the crashing of thunder in the skies, all the sobbings of Gehenna, and its God scattering empires as the wind scatters clouds.

They read it on Sunday at the hour of vespers, while the bell was ringing.

One day they went to mass, and then came back. It was a kind of recreation at the end of the week. The Count and Countess de Faverges bowed to them from the distance, a circumstance which was remarked. The justice of the peace said to them with blinking eyes:

"Excellent! You have my approval."

All the village dames now sent them consecrated bread. The Abbé Jeufroy paid them a visit; they returned it; friendly intercourse followed; and the priest avoided talking about religion.

They were astonished at this reserve, so much so that Pécuchet, with an assumption of indifference, asked him what was the way to set about obtaining faith.

"Practise first of all."

They began to practise, the one with hope, the other with defiance, Bouvard being convinced that he would never be a devotee. For a month he regularly followed all the services; but, unlike Pécuchet, he did not wish to subject himself to Lenten fare.

Was this a hygienic measure? We know what hygiene is worth. A matter of the proprieties? Down with the proprieties! A mark of submission towards the Church? He laughed at it just as much; in short, he declared the rule absurd, pharisaical, and contrary to the spirit of the Gospel.

On Good Friday in other years they used to eat whatever Germaine served up to them. But on this occasion Bouvard ordered a beefsteak. He sat down and cut up the meat, and Marcel, scandalised, kept staring at him, while Pécuchet gravely took the skin off his slice of codfish.

Bouvard remained with his fork in one hand, his knife in the other. At length, making up his mind, he raised a mouthful to his lips. All at once his hands began to tremble, his heavy countenance grew pale, his head fell back.

"Are you ill?"

"No. But——" And he made an avowal. In consequence of his education (it was stronger than himself), he could not eat meat on this day for fear of dying.

Pécuchet, without misusing his victory, took advantage of it to live in his own fashion. One evening he returned home with a look of sober joy imprinted on his face, and, letting the word escape, said that he had just been at confession.

Thereupon they argued about the importance of confession.

Bouvard acknowledged that of the early Christians, which was made publicly: the modern is too easy. However, he did not deny that this examination concerning ourselves might be an element of progress, a leaven of morality.

Pécuchet, desirous of perfection, searched for his vices: for some time past the puffings of pride were gone. His taste for work freed him from idleness; as for gluttony, nobody was more moderate. Sometimes he was carried away by anger.

He made a vow that he would be so no more.

In the next place, it would be necessary to acquire the virtues: first of all, humility, that is to say, to believe yourself incapable of any merit, unworthy of the least recompense, to immolate your spirit, and to place yourself so low that people may trample you under their feet like the mud of the roads. He was far as yet from these dispositions.

Another virtue was wanting in him—chastity. For inwardly he regretted Mélie, and the pastel of the lady in the Louis XV. dress disturbed him by her ample display of bosom. He shut it up in a cupboard, and redoubled his modesty, so much so that he feared to cast glances at his own person.

In order to mortify himself, Pécuchet gave up his little glass after meals, confined himself to four pinches of snuff in the day, and even in the coldest weather he did not any longer put on his cap.

One day, Bouvard, who was fastening up the vine, placed a ladder against the wall of the terrace near the house, and, without intending it, found himself landed in Pécuchet's room.

His friend, naked up to the middle, first gently smacked his shoulders with the cat-o'-nine-tails without quite undressing; then, getting animated, pulled off his shirt, lashed his back, and sank breathless on a chair.

Bouvard was troubled, as if at the unveiling of a mystery on which he should not have gazed.

For some time he had noticed a greater cleanliness about the floor, fewer holes in the napkins, and an improvement in the diet—changes which were due to the intervention of Reine, the curé's housekeeper. Mixing up the affairs of the Church with those of her kitchen, strong as a ploughman, and devoted though disrespectful, she gained admittance into households, gave advice, and became mistress in them. Pécuchet placed implicit confidence in her experience.

On one occasion she brought to him a corpulent man with narrow eyes like a Chinaman, and a nose like a vulture's beak. This was M. Gouttman, a dealer in pious articles. He unpacked some of them shut up in boxes under the cart-shed: a cross, medals, and beads of all sizes; candelabra for oratories, portable altars, tinsel bouquets, and sacred hearts of blue pasteboard, St. Josephs with red beards, and porcelain crucifixes. The price alone stood in his way.

Gouttman did not ask for money. He preferred barterings; and, having gone up to the museum, he offered a number of his wares for their collection of old iron and lead.

They appeared hideous to Bouvard. But Pécuchet's glance, the persistency of Reine, and the bluster of the dealer were effectual in making him yield.

Gouttman, seeing him so accommodating, wanted the halberd in addition; Bouvard, tired of having exhibited its working, surrendered it. The entire valuation was made. "These gentlemen still owed a hundred francs." It was settled by three bills payable at three months; and they congratulated themselves on a good bargain.

Their acquisitions were distributed through the various rooms. A crib filled with hay and a cork cathedral decorated the museum.

On Pécuchet's chimney-piece there was a St. John the Baptist in wax; along the corridor were ranged the portraits of episcopal dignitaries; and at the bottom of the staircase, under a chained lamp, stood a Blessed Virgin in an azure mantle and a crown of stars. Marcel cleaned up those splendours, unable to imagine anything more beautiful in Paradise.

What a pity that the St. Peter was broken, and how nicely it would have done in the vestibule!

Pécuchet stopped sometimes before the old pit for composts, where he discovered the tiara, one sandal, and the tip of an ear; allowed sighs to escape him, then went on gardening, for now he combined manual labour with religious exercises, and dug the soil attired in the monk's habit, comparing himself to Bruno. This disguise might be a sacrilege. He gave it up.

But he assumed the ecclesiastical style, no doubt owing to his intimacy with the curé. He had the same smile, the same tone of voice, and, like the priest too, he slipped both hands with a chilly air into his sleeves up to the wrists. A day came when he was pestered by the crowing of the cock and disgusted with the roses; he no longer went out, or only cast sullen glances over the fields.

Bouvard suffered himself to be led to the May devotions. The children singing hymns, the gorgeous display of lilacs, the festoons of verdure, had imparted to him, so to speak, a feeling of imperishable youth. God manifested Himself to his heart through the fashioning of nests, the transparency of fountains, the bounty of the sun; and his friend's devotion appeared to him extravagant, fastidious.

"Why do you groan during mealtime?"

"We ought to eat with groans," returned Pécuchet, "for it was in that way that man lost his innocence"—a phrase which he had read in the Seminarist's Manual, two duodecimo volumes he had borrowed from M. Jeufroy: and he drank some of the water of La Salette, gave himself up with closed doors to ejaculatory prayers, and aspired to join the confraternity of St. Francis.

In order to obtain the gift of perseverance, he resolved to make a pilgrimage in honour of the Blessed Virgin. He was perplexed as to the choice of a locality. Should it be Nôtre Dame de Fourviers, de Chartres, d'Embrun, de Marseille, or d'Auray? Nôtre Dame de la Délivrande was nearer, and it suited just as well.

"You will accompany me?"

"I should look like a greenhorn," said Bouvard.

After all, he might come back a believer; he did not object to being one; and so he yielded through complaisance.

Pilgrimages ought to be made on foot. But forty-three kilometers would be trying; and the public conveyances not being adapted for meditation, they hired an old cabriolet, which, after a twelve hours' journey, set them down before the inn.

They got an apartment with two beds and two chests of drawers, supporting two water-jugs in little oval basins; and "mine host" informed them that this was "the chamber of the Capuchins" under the Terror. There La Dame de la Délivrande had been concealed with so much precaution that the good fathers said mass there clandestinely.

This gave Pécuchet pleasure; and he read aloud a sketch of the history of the chapel, which had been taken downstairs into the kitchen.

It had been founded in the beginning of the second century by St. Régnobert, first bishop of Lisieux, or by St. Ragnebert, who lived in the seventh, or by Robert the Magnificent in the middle of the eleventh.

The Danes, the Normans, and, above all, the Protestants, had burnt and ravaged it at various epochs.

About 1112, the original statue was discovered by a sheep, which indicated the place where it was by tapping with its foot in a field of grass; and on this spot Count Baudouin erected a sanctury.

"'Her miracles are innumerable. A merchant of Bayeux, taken captive by the Saracens, invoked her: his fetters fell off, and he escaped. A miser found a nest of rats in his corn loft, appealed to her aid, and the rats went away. The touch of a medal, which had been rubbed over her effigy, caused an old materialist from Versailles to repent on his death-bed. She gave back speech to Sieur Adeline, who lost it for having blasphemed; and by her protection, M. and Madame de Becqueville had sufficient strength to live chastely in the married state.

"'Amongst those whom she cured of irremediable diseases are mentioned Mademoiselle de Palfresne, Anne Lirieux, Marie Duchemin, François Dufai, and Madame de Jumillac née d'Osseville.

"'Persons of high rank have visited her : Louis XI., Louis XIII., two daughters of Gaston of Orléans, Cardinal Wiseman, Samirrhi, patriarch of Antioch, Monseigneur Véroles, vicar apostolic of Manchuria; and the Archbishop of Quelen came to return thanks to her for the conversion of Prince Talleyrand.'"

"She might," said Pécuchet, "convert you also!"

Bouvard, already in bed, gave vent to a species of grunt, and presently was fast asleep.

Next morning at six o'clock they entered the chapel.

Another was in course of construction. Canvas and boards blocked up the nave; and the monument, in a rococo style, displeased Bouvard, above all, the altar of red marble with its Corinthian pilasters.

The miraculous statue, in a niche at the left of the choir, was enveloped in a spangled robe. The beadle came up with a wax taper for each of them. He fixed it in a kind of candlestick overlooking the balustrade, asked for three francs, made a bow, and disappeared.

Then they surveyed the votive offerings. Inscriptions on slabs bore testimony to the gratitude of the faithful. They admired two swords in the form of a cross presented by a pupil of the Polytechnic School, brides' bouquets, military medals, silver hearts, and in the corner, along the floor, a forest of crutches.

A priest passed out of the sacristy carrying the holy pyx.

When he had remained for a few minutes at the bottom of the altar, he ascended the three steps, said the *Oremus*, the *Introit*, and the *Kyrie*, which the boy who served mass recited all in one breath on bended knees.

The number present was small—a dozen or fifteen old women. The rattling of their beads could be heard accompanying the noise of a hammer driving in stones. Pécuchet bent over his prie-dieu and responded to the "Amens." During the elevation, he implored Our Lady to send him a constant and indestructible faith. Bouvard, in a chair beside him, took up his Euchology, and stopped at the litany of the Blessed Virgin.

"Most pure, most chaste, most venerable, most amiable, most powerful—Tower of ivory—House of gold—Gate of the morning."

These words of adoration, these hyperboles drew him towards the being who has been the object of so

much reverence. He dreamed of her as she is represented in church paintings, above a mass of clouds,
cherubims at her feet, the Infant Jesus on her breast —
Mother of tendernesses, upon whom all the sorrows of
the earth have a claim — ideal of woman carried up to
heaven; for man exalts that love arising out of the
depths of the soul, and his highest aspiration is to rest
upon her heart.

The mass was finished. They passed along by the
dealers' sheds which lined the walls in front of the
church. They saw there images, holy-water basins,
urns with fillets of gold, Jesus Christs made of cocoa-
nuts, and ivory chaplets; and the sun brought into
prominence the rudeness of the paintings, the hideous-
ness of the drawings. Bouvard, who had some
abominable specimens at his own residence, was indulgent towards these. He bought a little Virgin of blue
paste. Pécuchet contented himself with a rosary as a
memento.

The dealers called out: "Come on! come on!
For five francs, for three francs, for sixty centimes,
for two sous, don't refuse Our Lady!"

The two pilgrims sauntered about without making
any selections from the proffered wares. Uncompli-
mentary remarks were made about them.

"What is it they want, these creatures?"

"Perhaps they are Turks."

"Protestants, rather."

A big girl dragged Pécuchet by the frock-coat; an
old man in spectacles placed a hand on his shoulder;
all were bawling at the same time; and a number of
them left their sheds, and, surrounding the pair, redoubled their solicitations and effronteries.

Bouvard could not stand this any longer.

10—2

"Let us alone, for God's sake!"

The crowd dispersed. But one fat woman followed them for some distance, and exclaimed that they would repent of it.

When they got back to the inn they found Gouttman in the café. His business called him to these quarters, and he was talking to a man who was examining accounts at a table.

This person had a leather cap, a very wide pair of trousers, a red complexion, and a good figure in spite of his white hair: he had the appearance at the same time of a retired officer and an old strolling player.

From time to time he rapped out an oath; then, when Gouttman replied in a mild tone, he calmed down at once and passed to another part of the accounts.

Bouvard who had been closely watching him, at the end of a quarter of an hour came up to his side.

"Barberou, I believe?"

"Bouvard!" exclaimed the man in the cap, and they embraced each other.

Barberou had in the course of twenty years experienced many changes of fortune. He had been editor of a newspaper, an insurance agent, and manager of an oyster-bed.

"I will tell you all about it," he said.

At last, having returned to his original calling, he was travelling for a Bordeaux house, and Gouttman, who took care of the diocese, disposed of wines for him to the ecclesiastics. "But," he hurriedly added, "you must pardon me one minute; then I shall be at your service."

He was proceeding with the examination of the accounts, and all of a sudden he jumped up excitedly.

"What! two thousand?"

"Certainly."

"Ha! it's wrong, that's what it is!"

"What do you say?"

"I say that I've seen Hérambert myself," replied Barberou in a passion. "The invoice makes it four thousand. No humbug!"

The dealer was not put out of countenance.

"Well, it discharges you — what next?"

Barberou, as he stood there with his face at first pale and then purple, impressed Bouvard and Pécuchet with the apprehension that he was about to strangle Gouttman.

He sat down, folded his arms, and said:

"You are a vile rascal, you must admit"

"No insults, Monsieur Barberou. There are witnesses. Be careful!"

"I'll bring an action against you!"

"Ta! ta! ta!" Then having fastened together his books, Gouttman lifted the brim of his hat: "I wish you luck on't!" With these words he went off.

Barberou explained the facts: For a credit of a thousand francs doubled by a succession of renewals with interest, he had delivered to Gouttman three thousand francs' worth of wines. This would pay his debt with a profit of a thousand francs; but, on the contrary, he owed three thousand on the transaction! His employers might dismiss him; they might even prosecute him!

"Blackguard! robber! dirty Jew! And this fellow dines at priests' houses! Besides, everything that touches the clerical headpiece ——"

And he went on railing against the priests, and he struck the table with such violence that the little statue was near falling.

" Gently!" said Bouvard.

"Hold on! What's this here?" And Barberou having removed the covering of the little Virgin: "A pilgrimage bauble! Yours?"

"'Tis mine," said Pécuchet.

"You grieve me," returned Barberou; "but I'll give you a wrinkle on that point. Don't be afraid." And as one must be a philosopher, and as there is no use in fretting, he invited them to come and lunch with him.

The three sat down together at table.

Barberou was agreeable, recalled old times, took hold of the maid-servant's waist, and wished to measure the breadth of Bouvard's stomach. He would soon see them again, and would bring them a droll book.

The idea of his visit was rather pleasant to them. They chatted about it in the omnibus for an hour, while the horse was trotting. Then Pécuchet shut his eyes. Bouvard also relapsed into silence. Internally he felt an inclination towards religion.

"M. Marescot had the day before called to make an important communication"—Marcel knew no more about it.

They did not see the notary till three days after; and at once he explained the matter.

Madame Bordin offered to buy the farm from M. Bouvard, and to pay him seven thousand five hundred francs a year.

She had been casting sheep's eyes on it since her youth, knew the boundaries and lands all around it, its defects and its advantages; and this desire consumed her like a cancer.

For the good lady, like a true Norman, cherished above everything landed estate, less for the security

of the capital than for the happiness of treading on
soil that belonged to herself. In that hope she had
devoted herself to inquiries and inspections from day
to day, and had practised prolonged economies; and
she waited with impatience for Bouvard's answer.

He was perplexed, not desiring that Pécuchet one
day should be fortuneless; but it was necessary to
seize the opportunity—which was the result of the
pilgrimage, for the second time Providence had
shown itself favourable to them. They proposed the
following conditions: An annual payment, not of
seven thousand five hundred francs, but of six thousand francs, provided it should pass to the survivor.

Marescot made the point that one of them was in
delicate health. The constitution of the other gave
him an apoplectic tendency. Madame Bordin, carried
away by her ruling passion, signed the contract.

Bouvard got into a melancholy frame of mind
about it. Somebody might desire his death; and this
reflection inspired him with serious thoughts, ideas
about God and eternity.

Three days after, M. Jeufroy invited them to the
annual dinner which it was his custom to give to
his colleagues. The dinner began at two o'clock in
the afternoon, and was to finish at eleven at night.

Perry was used at it as a beverage, and puns
were circulated. The Abbé Pruneau, before they
broke up, composed an acrostic; M. Bougon performed card-tricks; and Cerpet, a young curate, sang
a little ballad which bordered on gallantry.

The curé frequently came to see them. He presented religion under graceful colours. And, after all,
what risk would they run? So Bouvard expressed
his willingness to approach the holy table shortly,

and Pécuchet was to participate in the sacrament on the same occasion.

The great day arrived. The church, on account of the first communions, was thronged with worshippers. The village shopkeepers and their womenfolk were crowded close together in their seats, and the common people either remained standing up behind or occupied the gallery over the church door.

What was about to take place was inexplicable — so Bouvard reflected; but reason does not suffice for the comprehension of certain things. Great men have admitted that. Let him do as much as they had done; and so, in a kind of torpor, he contemplated the altar, the censer, the tapers, with his head a little light, for he had eaten nothing, and experienced a singular weakness.

Pécuchet, by meditating on the Passion of Jesus Christ, excited himself to outbursts of love. He would have liked to offer his soul up to Him as well as the souls of others — and the ecstasies, the transports, the illumination of the saints, all beings, the entire universe. Though he prayed with fervour, the different parts of the mass seemed to him a little long.

At length the little boys knelt down on the first step of the altar, forming with their coats a black band, above which rose light or dark heads of hair at unequal elevations. Then the little girls took their places, with their veils falling from beneath their wreaths. From a distance they resembled a row of white clouds at the end of the choir.

Then it was the turn of the great personages.

The first on the gospel-side was Pécuchet; but, too much moved, no doubt, he kept swaying his head right and left. The curé found difficulty in putting the host into his mouth, and as he received it he turned up the whites of his eyes.

Bouvard, on the contrary, opened his jaws so widely, that his tongue hung over his lip like a streamer. On rising he jostled against Madame Bordin. Their eyes met. She smiled; without knowing the reason why, he reddened.

After Madame Bordin, Mademoiselle de Faverges, the countess, their lady companion, and a gentleman who was not known at Chavignolles approached the altar in a body.

The last two were Placquevent and Petit, the schoolmaster, and then, all of a sudden, Gorju made his appearance. He had got rid of the tuft on his chin, and, as he went back to his place, he had his arms crossed over his breast in a very edifying fashion.

The curé harangued the little boys. Let them take care later on in life not to act like Judas, who betrayed his God, but to preserve always their robe of innocence.

Pécuchet was regretting his when there was a sudden moving of the seats: the mothers were impatient to embrace their children.

The parishioners, on their way out, exchanged felicitations. Some shed tears. Madame de Faverges, while waiting for her carriage, turned round towards Bouvard and Pécuchet, and presented her future son-in-law: "Baron de Mahurot, engineer." The count was sorry not to have the pleasure of their company. He would return the following week. "Pray bear it in mind."

The carriage having now come up, the ladies of the château departed, and the throng dispersed.

They found a parcel inside their own grounds in the middle of the grass. The postman, as the house had been shut up, had thrown it over the wall. It was the work which Barberou had promised to send, *Examination of Christianity*, by Louis Hervieu, a former pupil of the Normal School. Pécuchet would have nothing to say to it, and Bouvard had no desire to make himself acquainted with it.

He had been repeatedly told that the sacrament would transform him. For several days he awaited its blossomings in his conscience. He remained the same as ever, and a painful astonishment took possession of him.

What! The Flesh of God mingles with our flesh, and it produces no effect there! The Thought which governs the world does not illuminate our spirits! The Supreme Power abandons us to impotence!

M. Jeufroy, while reassuring him, prescribed for him the catechism of the Abbé Gaume.

On the other hand, Pécuchet's devotion had become developed. He would have liked to communicate under two species, kept singing psalms as he walked along the corridor, and stopped the people of Chavignolles to argue with, and to convert them. Vaucorbeil laughed in his face; Girbal shrugged his shoulders; and the captain called him "Tartuffe."

It was now thought that they were going too far.

It is an excellent custom to consider things as so many symbols. If the thunder rumbles, imagine to yourself the Last Judgment; at sight of a cloudless sky, think of the abode of the blessed; say to yourself in your walks that every step brings you nearer to death. Pécuchet observed this method.

When he took hold of his clothes, he thought of the carnal envelope in which the Second Person of the Trinity was clad; the ticking of the clock recalled to him the beatings of His heart, and the prick of a pin the nails of the Cross. But in vain did he remain on his knees for hours and multiply his fasts and strain his imagination. He did not succeed in getting detached from self; it was impossible to attain to perfect contemplation.

He had recourse to mystic authors: St. Theresa, John of the Cross, Louis of Granada, Simpoli, and, of the more modern, Monseigneur Chaillot. Instead of the sublimities which he expected, he encountered only platitudes, a very disjointed style, fulgid imagery, and many comparisons drawn from lapidaries' shops.

He learned, however, that there is an active purgation and a passive purgation, an internal vision and an external vision, four kinds of prayers, nine excellencies in love, six degrees in humility, and that the wounding of the soul is not very different from spiritual theft.

Some points embarrassed him.

"Since the flesh is accursed, how is it that we are bound to thank God for the boon of existence?" "What proportion must be observed between the fear indispensable to the salvation and the hope which is no less so?" "Where is the sign of grace?" etc.

M. Jeufroy's answers were simple.

"Don't worry yourself. By desiring to sift everything we rush along a perilous slope."

The *Catechism of Perseverance*, by Gaume, had disgusted Pécuchet so much that he took up Louis

Hervieu's book. It was a summary of modern exegesis, prohibited by the government. Barberou, as a republican, had bought the book.

It awakened doubts in Bouvard's mind, and, first of all, on original sin. "If God had created man peccable, He ought not to punish him; and evil is anterior to the Fall, since there were already volcanoes and wild beasts. In short, this dogma upsets my notions of justice."

"What would you have?" said the curé. "It is one of those truths about which everybody is agreed, without being able to furnish proofs of it; and we ourselves make the crimes of their fathers rebound on the children. Thus morality and law justify this decree of Providence, since we find it in nature."

Bouvard shook his head. He had also doubts about hell.

"For every punishment should look to the amelioration of the guilty person, which is impossible where the penalty is eternal; and how many are enduring it? Just think! All the ancients, the Jews, the Mussulmans, the idolaters, the heretics, and the children who have died without baptism — those children created by God, and for what end? — for the purpose of being punished for a sin which they did not commit!"

"Such is St. Augustine's opinion," added the curé; "and St. Fulgentius involves even the unborn child in damnation. The Church, it is true, has come to no decision on this matter. One remark, however. It is not God, but the sinner who damns himself; and the offence being infinite, since God is infinite, the punishment must be infinite. Is that all, sir?"

"Explain the Trinity to me," said Bouvard.

"With pleasure. Let us take a comparison: the three sides of a triangle, or rather our soul, which contains being, knowing, and willing; what we call faculty in the case of man is person in God. There is the mystery."

"But the three sides of the triangle are not each the triangle; these three faculties of the soul do not make three souls, and your persons of the Trinity are three Gods."

"Blasphemy!"

"So then there is only one person, one God, one substance affected in three ways!"

"Let us adore without understanding," said the curé.

"Be it so," said Bouvard. He was afraid of being taken for an atheist, and getting into bad odour at the château.

They now visited there three times a week, about five o'clock in winter, and the cup of tea warmed them. The count's manners recalled the ease of the ancient court; the countess, placid and plump, exhibited much discernment about everything. Mademoiselle Yolande, their daughter, was the type of the young person, the angel of "keepsakes"; and Madame de Noares, their lady companion, resembled Pécuchet in having a pointed nose like him.

The first time they entered the drawing-room she was defending somebody.

"I assure you he is changed. His gift is a proof of it."

This somebody was Gorju. He had made the betrothed couple an offer of a Gothic prie-dieu. It was brought. The arms of the two houses appeared on

it in coloured relief. M. de Mahurot seemed satisfied
with it, and Madame de Noares said to him:

"You will remember my *protégés?*"

Then she brought in two children, a boy of a
dozen years and his sister, who was perhaps ten.
Through the holes in their rags could be seen their
limbs, reddened with cold. The one was shod in old
slippers, the other wore only one wooden shoe.
Their foreheads disappeared under their hair, and
they stared around them with burning eyeballs like
famished wolves.

Madame de Noares told how she had met them
that morning on the high-road. Placquevent could
not give any information about them.

They were asked their names.

"Victor — Victorine."

"Where was their father?"

"In jail."

"And what was he doing before that?"

"Nothing."

"Their country?"

"St. Pierre."

"But which St. Pierre?"

The two little ones for sole response, said, snivel-
ling:

"Don't know — don't know."

Their mother was dead, and they were begging.

Madame de Noares explained how dangerous it
would be to abandon them; she moved the countess.
piqued the count's sense of honour, was backed up
by mademoiselle, pressed the matter — succeeded.

The gamekeeper's wife would take charge of them.
Later, work would be found for them, and, as they
did not know how to read or write, Madame de

Noares gave them lessons herself, with a view to preparing them for catechism.

When M. Jeufroy used to come to the château, the two youngsters would be sent for; he would question them, and then deliver a lecture, into which he would import a certain amount of display on account of his audience.

On one occasion, when the abbé had discoursed about the patriarchs, Bouvard, on the way home with him and Pécuchet, disparaged them very much.

"Jacob is notorious for his thieveries, David for his murders, Solomon for his debaucheries."

The abbé replied that we should look further into the matter. Abraham's sacrifice is a prefiguration of the Passion; Jacob is another type of the Messiah, just like Joseph, like the Brazen Serpent, like Moses.

"Do you believe," said Bouvard, "that he composed the 'Pentateuch'?"

"Yes, no doubt."

"And yet his death is recorded in it; the same observation applies to Joshua; and, as for the Judges, the author informs us that, at the period whose history he was writing, Israel had not yet kings. The work was, therefore, written under the Kings. The Prophets, too, astonish me."

"He's going to deny the Prophets now!"

"Not at all! but their overheated imagination saw Jehovah under different forms — that of a fire, of a bush, of an old man, of a dove; and they were not certain of revelation since they are always asking for a sign."

"Ha! and where have you found out these nice things?"

"In Spinoza."

At this word, the curé jumped.

"Have you read him?"

"God forbid!"

"Nevertheless, sir, science ——"

"Sir, no one can be a scholar without being a Christian."

Science furnished a subject for sarcasms on his part:

"Will it make an ear of corn sprout, this science of yours? What do we know?" he said.

But he did know that the world was created for us; he did know that archangels are above the angels; he did know that the human body will rise again such as it was about the age of thirty.

His ecclesiastical self-complacency provoked Bouvard, who, through want of confidence in Louis Hervieu, had written to Varlot; and Pécuchet, better informed, asked M. Jeufroy for explanations of Scripture.

The six days of Genesis mean six great epochs. The pillage of the precious vessels made by the Jews from the Egyptians must be interpreted to mean intellectual riches, the arts of which they had stolen the secret. Isaiah did not strip himself completely, *nudus* in Latin signifying "up to the hips": thus Virgil advises people to go naked in order to plough, and that writer would not have given a precept opposed to decency. Ezekiel devouring a book has nothing extraordinary in it; do we not speak of devouring a pamphlet, a newspaper?

"But if we see metaphors everywhere, what will become of the facts?"

The abbé maintained, nevertheless, that they were realities.

This way of understanding them appeared disloyal to Pécuchet. He pushed his investigations further, and brought a note on the contradictions of the Bible.

"Exodus teaches us that for forty years they offered up sacrifices in the desert; according to Amos and Jeremiah they offered up none. Paralipomenon and the book of Esdras are not in agreement as to the enumeration of the people. In Deuteronomy, Moses saw the Lord face to face; according to Exodus, he could not see Him. Where, then, is the inspiration?"

"An additional ground for admitting it," replied M. Jeufroy smiling. "Impostors have need of connivance; the sincere take no such precautions. In perplexity, have recourse to the Church. She is always infallible."

"On whom does her infallibility depend?"

"The Councils of Basle and of Constance attribute it to the councils. But often the councils are at variance — witness that which decided in favour of Athanasius and of Arius; those of Florence and Lateran award it to the Pope."

"But Adrian VI. declares that the Pope may be mistaken, like any other person."

"Quibbles! All that does not affect the permanence of dogma."

"Louis Hervieu's work points out the variations: baptism was formerly reserved for adults, extreme unction was not a sacrament till the ninth century, the Real Presence was decreed in the eighth, purgatory recognised in the fifteenth, the Immaculate Conception is a thing of yesterday."

And so it came to pass that Pécuchet did not

know what to think of Jesus. Three Evangelists make him out to be a man. In one passage of St. John he appears to be equal to God; in another, all the same, to acknowledge himself His inferior.

The abbé rejoined by citing the letter of King Abgar, the acts of Pilate, and the testimony of the sibyls, "the foundation of which is genuine." He found the Virgin again amongst the Gauls, the announcement of a Redeemer in China, the Trinity everywhere, the Cross on the cap of the Grand Lama, and in Egypt in the closed hands of the gods; and he even exhibited an engraving representing a nilometer, which, according to Pécuchet, was a phallus.

M. Jeufroy secretly consulted his friend Pruneau, who searched for proofs for him in the authors. A conflict of erudition was waged, and, lashed by conceit, Pécuchet became abstruse, mythological. He compared the Virgin to Isis, the Eucharist to the Homa of the Persians, Bacchus to Moses, Noah's ark to the ship of Xithurus. These analogies demonstrated to his satisfaction the identity of religions.

But there cannot be several religions, since there is only one God. And when he was at the end of his arguments, the man in the cassock exclaimed: "It is a mystery!"

"What is the meaning of that word? Want of knowledge: very good. But if it denotes a thing the mere statement of which involves contradiction, it is a piece of stupidity."

And now Pécuchet would never let M. Jeufroy alone. He would surprise him in the garden, wait for him in the confessional, and take up the argument again in the sacristy.

The priest had to invent plans in order to escape from him.

One day, after he had started for Sassetot on a sick call, Pécuchet proceeded along the road in front of him in such a way as to render conversation inevitable.

It was an evening about the end of August. The red sky began to darken, and a large cloud lowered above them, regular at the base and forming volutes at the top.

Pécuchet at first talked about indifferent subjects, then, having slipped out the word "martyr":

"How many do you think there were of them?"

"A score of millions at least."

"Their number is not so great, according to Origen."

"Origen, you know, is open to suspicion."

A big gust of wind swept past, violently shaking the grass beside the ditches and the two rows of young elm trees that stretched towards the end of the horizon.

Pécuchet went on:

"Amongst the martyrs we include many Gaulish bishops killed while resisting the barbarians, which is no longer the question at issue."

"Do you wish to defend the emperors?"

According to Pécuchet, they had been calumniated.

"The history of the Theban legion is a fable. I also question Symphorosa and her seven sons, Felicitas and her seven daughters, and the seven virgins of Ancyra condemned to violation, though septuagenarians, and the eleven thousand virgins of St. Ursula, of whom one companion was called *Undecemilla*, a

10—3

name taken for a figure; still more, the ten martyrs of Alexandria!"

"And yet—and yet they are found in authors worthy of credit."

Raindrops fell, and the curé unrolled his umbrella; and Pécuchet, when he was under it, went so far as to maintain that the Catholics had made more martyrs than the Jews, the Mussulmans, the Protestants, and the Freethinkers—than all those of Rome in former days.

The priest exclaimed:

"But we find ten persecutions from the reign of Nero to that of Cæsar Galba!"

"Well! and the massacres of the Albigenses? and St. Bartholomew? and the revocation of the Edict of Nantes?"

"Deplorable excesses, no doubt; but you do not mean to compare these people to St. Étienne, St. Lawrence, Cyprian, Polycarp, a crowd of missionaries?"

"Excuse me! I will remind you of Hypatia, Jerome of Prague, John Huss, Bruno, Vanini, Anne Dubourg!"

The rain increased, and its drops dashed down with such force that they rebounded from the ground like little white rockets.

Pécuchet and M. Jeufroy walked on slowly, pressed close to one another, and the curé said:

"After abominable tortures they were flung into vessels of boiling water."

"The Inquisition made use of the same kind of torture, and it burned very well for you."

"Illustrious ladies were exhibited to the public gaze in the *lupanars*."

"Do you believe Louis XIV.'s dragoons regarded decency?"

"And mark well that the Christians had done nothing against the State."

"No more had the Huguenots."

The wind swept the rain into the air. It clattered on the leaves, trickled at the side of the road; and the mud-coloured sky intermingled with the fields, which lay bare after the close of harvest. Not a root was to be seen. Only, in the distance, a shepherd's hut.

Pécuchet's thin overcoat had no longer a dry thread in it. The water ran along his spine, got into his boots, into his ears, into his eyes, in spite of the Amoros headpiece. The curé, while lifting up with one hand the tail of his cassock, uncovered his legs; and the points of his three-cornered hat sputtered the water over his shoulders, like the gargoyles of a cathedral.

They had to stop, and, turning their backs to the storm, they remained face to face, belly to belly, holding with their four hands the swaying umbrella.

M. Jeufroy had not interrupted his vindication of the Catholics.

"Did they crucify your Protestants, as was done to St. Simeon; or get a man devoured by two tigers, as happened to St. Ignatius?"

"But make some allowance for the number of women separated from their husbands, children snatched from their mothers, and the exile of the poor across the snow, in the midst of precipices. They huddled them together in prisons; just when they were at the point of death they were dragged along on the hurdle."

The abbé sneered. "You will allow me not to believe a word of it. And our martyrs are less doubtful. St. Blandina was delivered over naked in a net to a furious cow. St. Julia was beaten to death. St. Taracus, St. Probus, and St. Andronicus had their teeth broken with a hammer, their sides torn with iron combs, their hands pierced with reddened nails, and their scalps carried off."

"You are exaggerating," said Pécuchet. "The death of the martyrs was at that time an amplification of rhetoric."

"What! of rhetoric?"

"Why, yes; whilst what I relate to you, sir, is history. The Catholics in Ireland disembowelled pregnant women in order to take their children——"

"Never!"

"——and give them to the pigs."

"Come now!"

"In Belgium they buried women alive."

"What nonsense!"

"We have their names."

"And even so," objected the priest, angrily shaking his umbrella, "they cannot be called martyrs. There are no martyrs outside the Church."

"One word. If the value of a martyr depends on the doctrine, how could he serve to demonstrate its existence?"

The rain ceased; they did not speak again till they reached the village. But, on the threshold of the presbytery, the curé said:

"I pity you! really, I pity you!"

Pécuchet immediately told Bouvard about the wrangle. It had filled him with an antipathy to religion, and, an hour later, seated before a brushwood fire, they both read the *Curé Meslier*. These dull negations disgusted Pécuchet; then, reproaching himself for perhaps having misunderstood heroes, he ran through the history of the most illustrious martyrs in the Biography.

What a clamour from the populace when they entered the arena! and, if the lions and the jaguars were too quiet, the people urged them to come forward by their gestures and their cries. The victims could be seen covered with gore, smiling where they stood, with their gaze towards heaven. St. Perpetua bound up her hair in order that she might not look dejected.

Pécuchet began to reflect. The window was open, the night tranquil; many stars were shining. There must have passed through these martyrs' souls things of which we have no idea—a joy, a divine spasm! And Pécuchet, by dwelling on the subject, believed that he understood this emotion, and that he would have done the same himself.

"You?"

"Certainly."

"No fudge! Do you believe—yes or no?"

"I don't know."

He lighted a candle; then, his eyes falling on the crucifix in the alcove:

"How many wretches have sought help from that!"

And, after a brief silence:

"They have denaturalised Him. It is the fault of Rome—the policy of the Vatican."

But Bouvard admired the Church for her magnificence, and would have brought back the Middle Ages provided he might be a cardinal.

"You must admit I should have looked well in the purple."

Pécuchet's headpiece, placed in front of the fire, was not yet dry. While stretching it out he felt something in the lining, and out tumbled a medal of St. Joseph.

Madame de Noares wished to ascertain from Pécuchet whether he had not experienced some kind of change, bringing him happiness, and betrayed herself by her questions. On one occasion, whilst he was playing billiards, she had sewn the medal in his cap.

Evidently she was in love with him: they might marry; she was a widow, and he had had no suspicion of this attachment, which might have brought about his life's happiness.

Though he exhibited a more religious tendency than M. Bouvard, she had dedicated him to St. Joseph, whose succour is favourable to conversions.

No one knew so well as she all the beads and the indulgences which they procure, the effect of relics, the privileges of blessed waters. Her watch was attached to a chain that had touched the bonds of St. Peter. Amongst her trinkets glittered a pearl of gold, in imitation of the one in the church of Allouagne containing a tear of Our Lord; a ring on her little finger enclosed some of the hair of the curé of Ars, and, as she was in the habit of collecting simples for the sick, her apartment was like a sacristy combined with an apothecary's laboratory.

Her time was passed in writing letters, in visiting the poor, in dissolving irregular connections, and in distributing photographs of the Sacred Heart. A gentleman had promised to send her some "martyr's paste," a mixture of paschal wax and human dust taken from the Catacombs, and used in desperate cases in the shape of fly-blisters and pills. She promised some of it to Pécuchet.

He appeared shocked at such materialism.

In the evening a footman from the château brought him a basketful of little books relating pious phrases of the great Napoleon, witticisms of clergymen at inns, frightful deaths that had happened to atheists. All those things Madame de Noares knew by heart, along with an infinite number of miracles. She related several stupid ones — miracles without an object, as if God had performed them to excite the wonder of the world. Her own grandmother had locked up in a cupboard some prunes covered with a piece of linen, and when the cupboard was opened a year later they saw thirteen of them on the cloth forming a cross.

"Explain this to me."

This was the phrase she used after her marvellous tales, which she declared to be true, with the obstinacy of a mule. Apart from this she was a harmless woman of lively disposition.

On one occasion, however, she deviated from her character.

Bouvard was disputing with her about the miracle of Pezilla: this was a fruit-dish in which wafers had been hidden during the Revolution and which had become gilded of itself.

"Perhaps there was at the bottom a little yellow colour caused by humidity?"

"Not at all! I repeat it, there was not! The cause of the gilding was the contact with the Eucharist."

By way of proof she relied on the attestations of bishops.

"It is, they say, like a buckler, a — a palladium over the diocese of Perpignan. Ask Monsieur Jeufroy, then!"

Bouvard could not stand this kind of talk any longer; and, after he had looked over his Louis Hervieu, he took Pécuchet off with them.

The clergyman was finishing his dinner. Reine offered them chairs, and, at a gesture from her master, she went to fetch two little glasses, which she filled with Rosolio.

After this Bouvard explained what had brought him there.

The abbé did not reply candidly.

"Everything is possible to God, and the miracles are a proof of religion."

"However, there are laws of nature—"

"That makes no difference to Him. He sets them aside in order to instruct, to correct."

"How do you know whether He sets them aside?" returned Bouvard. "So long as Nature follows her routine we never bestow a thought on it, but in an extraordinary phenomenon we believe we see the hand of God."

"It may be there," replied the ecclesiastic; "and when an occurrence has been certified by witnesses——"

"The witnesses swallow everything, for there are spurious miracles."

The priest grew red.

"Undoubtedly; sometimes."

"How can we distinguish them from the genuine ones? If the genuine ones, given as proofs, have themselves need of proofs, why perform them?"

Reine interposed, and, preaching like her master, said it was necessary to obey.

"Life is a passage, but death is eternal."

"In short," suggested Bouvard, guzzling the Rosolio, "the miracles of former times are not better demonstrated than the miracles of to-day; analogous reasonings uphold those of Christians and Pagans."

The curé flung down his fork on the table.

"Again I tell you those miracles were spurious! There are no miracles outside of the Church."

"Stop!" said Pécuchet, "that is the same argument you used regarding the martyrs: the doctrine rests on the facts and the facts on the doctrine."

M. Jeufroy, having swallowed a glass of water, replied:

"Even while denying them you believe in them. The world which twelve fishermen converted—look at that! it seems to me a fine miracle."

"Not at all!"

Pécuchet gave a different account of the matter: "Monotheism comes from the Hebrews; the Trinity from the Indians; the Logos belongs to Plato, and the Virgin Mother to Asia."

No matter! M. Jeufroy clung to the supernatural and did not desire that Christianity should have humanly the least reason for its existence, though he saw amongst all peoples foreshadowings or deformations of it. The scoffing impiety of the eighteenth century he would have tolerated, but modern criticism, with its politeness, exasperated him.

"I prefer the atheist who blasphemes to the sceptic who cavils."

Then he looked at them with an air of bravado, as if to dismiss them.

Pécuchet returned home in a melancholy frame of mind. He had hoped for a reconciliation between faith and reason.

Bouvard made him read this passage from Louis Hervieu:

"In order to know the abyss which separates them, oppose their axioms.

"Reason says to you: 'The whole comprehends the part,' and faith replies to you: 'By substantiation, Jesus, while communicating with the apostles, had His body in His hand and His head in His mouth.'

"Reason says to you: 'No one is responsible for the crime of another,' and faith replies to you: 'By original sin.'

"Reason says to you: 'Three make three,' and faith declares that 'Three make one.'"

They no longer associated with the abbé.

It was the period of the war with Italy. The respectable people were trembling for the Pope. They were thundering against Victor Emmanuel. Madame de Noares went so far as to wish for his death. Bouvard and Pécuchet alone protested timidly.

When the door of the drawing-room flew open in front of them and they looked at themselves in the lofty mirrors, as they passed, whilst through the windows they caught a glimpse of the walks where glared above the grass the red waistcoat of a man-servant, they felt a sensation of delight; and the luxuriousness of their surroundings rendered them indulgent to the words that were uttered there.

The count lent them all the works of M. de Maistre. He expounded the principles contained in them before a circle of intimate friends — Hurel, the curé, the justice of the peace, the notary, and the baron, his future son-in-law, who used to come from time to time for twenty-four hours to the château.

"What is abominable," said the count, "is the spirit of 'eighty-nine. First of all they question the existence of God; then they dispute about government; then comes liberty — liberty for insults, for revolt, for enjoyments, or rather for plunder, so that religion and authority ought to proscribe the independents, the heretics. No doubt they will protest against what they call persecution, as if the executioners persecuted the criminals. Let me resume: No State without God! the law being unable to command respect unless it comes from on high, and, in fact, it is not a question of the Italians, but of determining which shall have the best of it, the Revolution or the Pope, Satan or Jesus Christ."

M. Jeufroy expressed his approval by monosyllables, Hurel by means of a smile, and the justice of the peace by nodding his head. Bouvard and Pécuchet kept their eyes fixed on the ceiling; Madame de Noares, the countess, and Yolande were making clothes for the poor, and M. de Mahurot, beside his betrothed, was turning over the leaves of a book.

Then came intervals of silence, during which everyone seemed to be absorbed in the investigation of a problem. Napoleon III. was no longer a saviour, and he had even given a deplorable example by allowing the masons at the Tuileries to work on Sunday.

"It ought not to be permitted," was the ordinary phrase of the count.

Social economy, fine arts, literature, history, scientific doctrines — on all he decided in his quality of Christian and father of a family; and would to God that the government, in this respect, exercised the same severity that he exhibited in his household! Authority alone is the judge of the dangers of science: spread too extensively, it inspires fatal ambitions in the breasts of the people. They were happier, these poor people, when the nobles and the bishops tempered the absolutism of the king. The manufacturers now make use of them. They are on the point of sinking into slavery.

And all looked back with regret to the old *régime*, Hurel through meanness, Coulon through ignorance, Marescot as a man of artistic tastes.

Bouvard, when he found himself at home once more, fortified his mind with a course of Lamettrie, Holbach, and others; whilst Pécuchet forsook a religion which had become a medium of government.

M. de Mahurot had communicated in order the better to charm the ladies, and, if he adopted it as a practice, it was in the interests of the servants.

A mathematician and *dilettante,* who played waltzes on the piano and admired Topffer, he was distinguished by a tasteful scepticism. What was said about feudal abuses, the Inquisition, and the Jesuits, was the result of prejudice. He extolled progress, though he despised everyone who was not a gentleman, or who had not come from the Polytechnic School!

M. Jeufroy likewise displeased the two friends. He believed in sorcery, made jokes about idolatry, declared that all idioms are derived from the Hebrew. His rhetoric lacked the element of novelty: it was invariably the stag at bay, honey and absinthe, gold and lead, perfumes, urns, and the comparison of the Christian soul to the soldier who ought to say in the face of sin: "Thou shalt not pass!"

In order to avoid his discourses they used to come to the château at as late an hour as possible.

One day, however, they encountered him there. He had been an hour awaiting his two pupils. Suddenly Madame de Noares entered.

"The little girl has disappeared. I am bringing Victor in. Ah! the wretch!"

She had found in his pocket a silver thimble which she had lost three days ago. Then, stifled with sobs:

"That is not all! While I was giving him a scolding, he turned his back on me!"

And, ere the count and countess could have said a word:

"However, it is my own fault: pardon me!"

She had concealed from them the fact that the two orphans were the children of Touache, who was now in prison.

What was to be done?

If the count sent them away they would be lost, and his act of charity would be taken for a caprice.

M. Jeufroy was not surprised. Since man is corrupt, our natural duty is to punish him in order to improve him.

Bouvard protested. Leniency was better. But the count once more expatiated on the iron hand indispensable for children as well as for the people. These two children were full of vices — the little girl was untruthful the boy brutish. This theft, after all, might have been excused, the impertinence never. Education should be the school of respect.

Therefore Sorel, the gamekeeper, would immediately administer to the youngster a good flogging.

M. de Mahurot, who had something to say to him, undertook the commission. He went to the anteroom for a gun, and called Victor, who had remained in the centre of the courtyard with downcast head.

"Follow me," said the baron. As the way to the gamekeeper's lodge turned off a little from Chavignolles, M. Jeufroy, Bouvard, and Pécuchet accompanied him.

At a hundred paces from the château, he begged them not to speak any more while he was walking along the wood.

The ground sloped down to the river's edge, where rose great blocks of stone. At sunset they looked like slabs of gold. On the opposite side the green hillocks were wrapped in shadow. A keen wind was blowing. Rabbits came out of their burrows, and began browsing on the grass.

A shot went off; a second; a third: and the rabbits jumped up, then rolled over. Victor flung himself on them to seize hold of them, and panted, soaking with perspiration.

"You have your clothes in nice condition!" said the baron.

There was blood on his ragged blouse.

Bouvard shrank from the sight of blood. He would not admit that it ever should be shed.

M. Jeufroy returned:

"Circumstances sometimes make it necessary. If the guilty person does not give his own, there is need of another's—a truth which the Redemption teaches us."

According to Bouvard, it had been of hardly any use, since nearly all mankind would be damned, in spite of the sacrifice of Our Lord.

"But every day He renews it in the Eucharist."

"And whatever be the unworthiness of the priest," said Pécuchet, "the miracle takes place at the words."

"There is the mystery, sir."

Meanwhile Victor had riveted his eyes on the gun, and he even tried to touch it.

"Down with your paws!" And M. de Mahurot took a long path through the wood.

The clergyman had placed Pécuchet on one side of him and Bouvard at the other, and said to the latter:

"Attention, you know. *Dobetur pueris.*"

Bouvard assured him that he humbled himself in the presence of the Creator, but was indignant at their having made Him a man. We fear His vengeance; we work for His glory. He has every virtue: an arm, an eye, a policy, a habitation.

"'Our Father, who art in heaven,' what does that mean?"

And Pécuchet added: "The universe has become enlarged; the earth is no longer its central point. It revolves amongst an infinite multitude of other worlds. Many of them surpass it in grandeur, and this belittlement of our globe shows a more sublime ideal of God.

"So, then, religion must change. Paradise is something infantile, with its blessed always in a state of contemplation, always chanting hymns, and looking from on high at the tortures of the damned. When one reflects that Christianity had for its basis an apple!"

The curé was annoyed. "Deny revelation; that would be simpler."

"How do you make out that God spoke?" said Bouvard.

"Prove that he did not speak!" said M. Jeufroy.

"Once again, who affirms it?"

"The Church."

"Nice testimony!"

This discussion bored M. de Mahurot, and, as he walked along: "Pray listen to the curé. He knows more than you."

Bouvard and Pécuchet made signs to indicate that they were taking another road; then, at Croix-Verte:

"A very good evening."

"Your servant," said the baron.

All this would be told to M. de Faverges, and perhaps a rupture would result. So much the worse. They felt that they were despised by those people of rank. They were never asked to dinner, and they were tired of Madame de Noares, with her continual remonstrances.

They could not, however, keep the De Maistre; and a fortnight after they returned to the château, not expecting to be welcomed, but they were. All the family were in the boudoir, and amongst those present were Hurel and, strangely enough, Foureau.

Correction had failed to correct Victor. He refused to learn his catechism; and Victorine gave utterance to vulgar words. In short, the boy should go to a reformatory, and the girl to a nunnery. Foureau was charged with carrying out the measure, and he was about to go when the countess called him back.

They were waiting for M. Jeufroy to fix the date of the marriage, which was to take place at the

mayor's office before being celebrated in the church, in order to show that they looked on civil marriage with contempt.

Foureau tried to defend it. The count and Hurel attacked it. What was a municipal function beside a priesthood?—and the baron would not have believed himself to be really wedded if he had been married only in the presence of a tri-coloured scarf.

"Bravo!" said M. Jeufroy, who had just come in. "Marriage having been established by Jesus Christ——"

Pécuchet stopped him: "In which Gospel? In the Apostolic times they respected it so little that Tertullian compares it to adultery."

"Oh! upon my word!"

"Yes, certainly! and it is not a sacrament. A sign is necessary for a sacrament. Show me the sign in marriage."

In vain did the curé reply that it represented the union of God with the Church.

"You do not understand Christianity either! And the law——"

"The law preserves the stamp of Christianity," said M. de Faverges. "Without that, it would permit polygamy."

A voice rejoined: "Where would be the harm?"

It was Bouvard, half hidden by a curtain.

"You might have many wives, like the Patriarchs, the Mormons, the Mussulmans, and nevertheless be an honest man."

"Never!" exclaimed the priest; "honesty consists in rendering what is due. We owe homage to God. So he who is not a Christian is not honest."

10—4

"Just as much as others," said Bouvard.

The count, believing that he saw in this rejoinder an attack on religion, extolled it. It had set free the slaves.

Bouvard referred to authorities to prove the contrary:

"St. Paul recommends them to obey their masters as they would obey Jesus. St. Ambrose calls servitude a gift of God. Leviticus, Exodus, and the Councils have sanctioned it. Bossuet treats it as a part of the law of nations. And Monseigneur Bouvier approves of it."

The count objected that, none the less, Christianity had developed civilisation.

"Ay, and idleness, by making a virtue of poverty."

"However, sir, the morality of the Gospel?"

"Ha! ha! not so moral! Those who labour only during the last hour are paid as much as those who labour from the first hour. To him who hath is given, and from him who hath not is taken away. As for the precept of receiving blows without returning them and of letting yourself be robbed, it encourages the audacious, the cowardly, and the dissolute."

They were doubly scandalised when Pécuchet declared that he liked Buddhism as well.

The priest burst out laughing.

"Ha! ha! ha! Buddhism!"

Madame de Noares lifted up her hands: "Buddhism!"

"What! Buddhism!" repeated the count.

"Do you understand it?" said Pécuchet to M. Jeufroy, who had become confused. "Well, then, learn something about it. Better than Christianity, and before it, it has recognised the nothingness of earthly things. Its practices are austere, its faithful more numerous than the entire body of Christians; and, as for incarnation, Vishnu had not merely one, but nine of them. So judge."

"Travellers' lies!" said Madame de Noares.

"Backed up by the Freemasons!" added the curé.

And all talking at the same time:

"Come, then, go on!"

"Very pretty!"

"For my part, I think it funny!"

"Not possible!"

Finally, Pécuchet, exasperated, declared that he would become a Buddhist!

"You are insulting Christian ladies," said the baron.

Madame de Noares sank into an armchair. The countess and Yolande remained silent. The count kept rolling his eyes; Hurel was waiting for his orders. The abbé, to contain himself, read his breviary.

This sight calmed M. de Favergcs; and, looking at the two worthies:

"Before you find fault with the Gospel, and that when there may be stains on your own lives, there is some reparation——"

"Reparation?"

"For stains?"

"Enough! gentlemen. You don't understand me." Then, addressing Foureau: "Sorel is informed about it. Go to him."

Bouvard and Pécuchet withdrew without bowing.

At the end of the avenue they all three gave vent to their indignation.

"They treated me as if I were a servant," grumbled Foureau; and, as his companions agreed with him, in spite of their recollection of the affair of the hemorrhoids, he exhibited towards them a kind of sympathy.

Road-menders were working in the neighbourhood. The man who was over them drew near: it was Gorju. They began to chat.

He was overseeing the macadamisation of the road, voted in 1848, and he owed this post to M. de Mahurot, the engineer. "The one that's going to marry Mademoiselle de Faverges. I suppose 'tis from the house below you were just coming?"

"For the last time," said Pécuchet gruffly.

Gorju assumed an innocent air. "A quarrel! Come, come!"

And if they could have seen his countenance when they had turned on their heels, they might have observed that he had scented the cause of it.

A little further on, they stopped before a trellised enclosure, inside which there were kennels, and also a red-tiled cottage.

Victorine was on the threshold. They heard dogs barking. The gamekeeper's wife came out. Knowing the object of the mayor's visit, she called to Victor. Everything was ready beforehand, and their outfit was contained in two pocket-handkerchiefs fastened together with pins.

"A pleasant journey," said the woman to the children, too glad to have no more to do with such vermin.

Was it their fault if they owed their birth to a convict father? On the contrary, they seemed very quiet, and did not even betray any alarm as to the place to which they were being conveyed.

Bouvard and Pécuchet watched them as they walked in front of them.

Victorine muttered some unintelligible words, with her little bundle over her arm, like a milliner carrying a bandbox.

Every now and then she would turn round, and Pécuchet, at the sight of her fair curls and her pretty figure, regretted that he had not such a child. Brought up under different conditions, she would be charming later. What happiness only to see her growing tall, to hear day after day her bird-like warbling, to kiss her when the fancy seized him!— and a feeling of tenderness, rising from his heart to his lips, made his eyes grow moist and somewhat oppressed his spirit.

Victor, like a soldier, had slung his baggage over his shoulder. He whistled, threw stones at the crows in the furrows, and went to cut switches off the trees.

Foureau called him back; and Bouvard, holding him by the hand, was delighted at feeling within his own those fingers of a robust and vigorous lad. The poor little wretch asked for nothing but to grow freely, like a flower in the open air! and he would rot between closed walls with tasks, punishment, a heap of tomfooleries! Bouvard was seized with pity, springing from a sense of revolt, a feeling of indignation against Fate, one of those fits of rage in which one longs to destroy government altogether.

"Jump about!" he said, "amuse yourself! Have a bit of fun as long as you can!"

The youngster scampered off.

His sister and he were to sleep at the inn, and at daybreak the messenger from Falaise would take Victor and set him down at the reformatory of Beaubourg; while a nun belonging to the orphanage of Grand-Camp would come to fetch Victorine.

Foureau having gone into these details, was once more lost in his own thoughts. But Bouvard wished to know how much the maintenance of the youngsters would cost.

"Bah! a matter perhaps of three hundred francs. The count has given me twenty-five for the first disbursements. What a stingy fellow!"

And, stung to the heart by the contempt shown towards his scarf, Foureau quickened his pace in silence.

Bouvard murmured: "They make me feel sad. I will take the charge of them."

"And so will I," said Pécuchet, the same idea having occurred to both of them.

No doubt there were impediments?

"None," returned Foureau. Besides, he had the right as mayor to entrust deserted children to whomsoever he thought fit. And, after a prolonged hesitation:

"Well, yes; take them! That will annoy *him*."

Bouvard and Pécuchet carried them off.

When they returned to their abode they found at the end of the staircase, under the Madonna, Marcel upon his knees praying with fervour. With his head thrown back, his eyes half closed, and his hare-lip gaping, he had the appearance of a fakir in ecstasy.

"What a brute!" said Bouvard.

"Why? He is perhaps attending to things that would make you envy him if you could only see them. Are there not two worlds entirely distinct? The aim of a process of reasoning is of less consequence than the manner of reasoning. What does the form of belief matter? The great thing is to believe."

Such were the objections of Pécuchet to Bouvard's observation.

CHAPTER X.

HEY procured a number of works relating to education, and resolved to adopt a system of their own. It was necessary to banish every metaphysical idea, and, in accordance with the experimental method, to follow in the lines of natural development. There was no haste, for the two pupils might forget what they had learned.

Though they had strong constitutions, Pécuchet wished, like a Spartan, to make them more hardy, to accustom them to hunger, thirst, and severe weather, and even insisted on having their feet badly shod in order that they might be prepared for colds. Bouvard was opposed to this.

The dark closet at the end of the corridor was used as their sleeping apartment. Its furniture consisted of two folding beds, two couches, and a jug. Above their heads the top window was open, and spiders crawled along the plaster. Often the children recalled to mind the interior of a cabin where they used to wrangle. One night their father came home with blood on his hands. Some time afterwards the

gendarmes arrived. After that they lived in a wood.
Men who made wooden shoes used to kiss their
mother. She died, and was carried off in a cart.
They used to get severe beatings; they got lost. Then
they could see once more Madame de Noares and
Sorel; and, without asking themselves the reason why
they were in this house, they felt happy there. But
they were disagreeably surprised when at the end of
eight months the lessons began again. Bouvard took
charge of the little girl, and Pécuchet of the boy.

Victor was able to distinguish letters, but did not
succeed in forming syllables. He stammered over
them, then stopped suddenly, and looked like an
idiot. Victorine put questions. How was it that
"ch" in "orchestra" had the sound of a "q," and
that of a "k" in "archæology." We must sometimes join two vowels and at other times separate
them. All this did not seem to her right. She grew
indignant at it.

The teachers gave instruction at the same hour in
their respective apartments, and, as the partition was
thin, these four voices, one soft, one deep, and two
sharp, made a hideous concert. To finish the business and to stimulate the youngsters by means of
emulation, they conceived the idea of making them
work together in the museum; and they proceeded to
teach them writing. The two pupils, one at each
end of the table, copied written words that were set
for them; but the position of their bodies was awk-
ward. It was necessary to straighten them; their
copybooks fell down; their pens broke, and their ink
bottles were turned upside down.

Victorine, on certain days, went on capitally for
about three minutes, then she would begin to scrawl,

and, seized with discouragement, she would sit with her eyes fixed on the ceiling. Victor was not long before he fell asleep, lying over his desk.

Perhaps they were distressed by it? Too great a strain was bad for young heads.

"Let us stop," said Bouvard.

There is nothing so stupid as to make children learn by heart; yet, if the memory is not exercised, it will go to waste, and so they taught the youngsters to recite like parrots the first fables of La Fontaine. The children expressed their approval of the ant that heaped up treasure, of the wolf that devoured the lamb, and of the lion that took everyone's share.

When they had become more audacious, they spoiled the garden. But what amusement could be provided for them?

Jean Jacques Rousseau in *Emile* advises the teacher to get the pupil to make his own playthings. Bouvard could not contrive to make a hoop or Pécuchet to sew up a ball. They passed on to toys that were instructive, such as cut-paper work. Pécuchet showed them his microscope. When the candle was lighted, Bouvard would sketch with the shadow of his finger on the wall the profile of a hare or a pig. But the pupils grew tired of it.

Writers have gone into raptures about the delightfulness of an open-air luncheon or a boating excursion. Was it possible for them really to have such recreations? Fénelon recommends from time to time "an innocent conversation." They could not invent one. So they had to come back to the lessons—the multiplying bowls, the erasures of their scrawlings, and the process of teaching them how to read by copying

printed characters. All had proved failures, when
suddenly a bright idea struck them.

As Victor was prone to gluttony, they showed
him the name of a dish: he soon ran through *Le
Cuisinier Français* with ease. Victorine, being a
coquette, was promised a new dress if she wrote to
the dressmaker for it: in less than three weeks she
accomplished this feat. This was playing on their
vices — a pernicious method, no doubt; but it had
succeeded.

Now that they had learned to read and write,
what should they be taught? Another puzzle.

Girls have no need of learning, as in the case of
boys. All the same, they are usually brought up like
mere animals, their sole intellectual baggage being
confined to mystical follies.

Is it expedient to teach them languages? "Spanish and Italian," the Swan of Cambray lays down,
"scarcely serve any purpose save to enable people to
read dangerous books."

Such a motive appeared silly to them. However,
Victorine would have to do only with these languages;
whereas English is more widely used. Pécuchet proceeded to study the rules of the language. He
seriously demonstrated the mode of expressing the
"th" — "like this, now, *the, the, the.*"

But before instructing a child we must be acquainted with its aptitudes. They may be divined by
phrenology. They plunged into it, then sought to
verify its assertions by experiments on their own persons. Bouvard exhibited the bumps of benevolence,
imagination, veneration, and amorous energy — *vulgo,*
eroticism. On Pécuchet's temples were found philosophy and enthusiasm allied with a crafty disposition.

Such, in fact, were their characters. What surprised them more was to recognise in the one as well as in the other a propensity towards friendship, and, charmed with the discovery, they embraced each other with emotion.

They next made an examination of Marcel. His greatest fault, of which they were not ignorant, was an excessive appetite. Nevertheless Bouvard and Pécuchet were dismayed to find above the top of the ear, on a level with the eye, the organ of alimentivity. With advancing years their servant would perhaps become like the woman in the Salpêtrière, who every day ate eight pounds of bread, swallowed at one time fourteen different soups, and at another sixty bowls of coffee. They might not have enough to keep him.

The heads of their pupils presented no curious characteristics. No doubt they had gone the wrong way to work with them. A very simple expedient enabled them to develop their experience.

On market days they insinuated themselves among groups of country people on the green, amid the sacks of oats, the baskets of cheese, the calves and the horses, indifferent to the jostlings; and whenever they found a young fellow with his father, they asked leave to feel his skull for a scientific purpose. The majority vouchsafed no reply; others, fancying it was pomatum for ringworm of the scalp, refused testily. A few, through indifference, allowed themselves to be led towards the porch of the church, where they would be undisturbed.

One morning, just as Bouvard and Pécuchet were beginning operations, the curé suddenly presented himself, and seeing what they were about, denounced phrenology as leading to materialism and to fatalism.

The thief, the assassin, the adulterer, have henceforth only to cast the blame of their crimes on their bumps.

Bouvard retorted that the organ predisposes towards the act without forcing one to do it. From the fact that a man has in him the germ of a vice, there is nothing to show that he will be vicious.

"However, I wonder at the orthodox, for, while upholding innate ideas, they reject propensities. What a contradiction!"

But phrenology, according to M. Jeufroy, denied Divine Omnipotence, and it was unseemly to practise under the shadow of the holy place, in the very face of the altar.

"Take yourselves off! No!—take yourselves off!"

They established themselves in the shop of Ganot, the hairdresser. Bouvard and Pécuchet went so far as to treat their subjects' relations to a shave or a clip. One afternoon the doctor came to get his hair cut. While seating himself in the armchair he saw in the glass the reflection of the two phrenologists passing their fingers over a child's pate.

"So you are at these fooleries?" he said.

"Why foolery?"

Vaucorbeil smiled contemptuously, then declared that there were not several organs in the brain. Thus one man can digest food which another cannot digest. Are we to assume that there are as many stomachs in the stomach as there are varieties of taste?

They pointed out that one kind of work is a relaxation after another; an intellectual effort does not strain all the faculties at the same time; each has its distinct seat.

"The anatomists have not discovered it," said Vaucorbeil.

"That's because they have dissected badly," replied Pécuchet.

"What?"

"Oh, yes! they cut off slices without regard to the connection of the parts"—a phrase out of a book which recurred to his mind.

"What a piece of nonsense!" exclaimed the physician. "The cranium is not moulded over the brain, the exterior over the interior. Gall is mistaken, and I defy you to justify his doctrine by taking at random three persons in the shop."

The first was a country woman, with big blue eyes.

Pécuchet, looking at her, said:

"She has a good memory."

Her husband attested the fact, and offered himself for examination.

"Oh! you, my worthy fellow, it is hard to lead you."

According to the others, there was not in the world such a headstrong fellow.

The third experiment was made on a boy who was accompanied by his grandmother.

Pécuchet observed that he must be fond of music.

"I assure you it is so," said the good woman. "Show these gentlemen, that they may see for themselves."

He drew a Jew's-harp from under his blouse and began blowing into it.

There was a crashing sound—it was the violent slamming of the door by the doctor as he went out.

They were no longer in doubt about themselves, and summoning their two pupils, they resumed the analysis of their skull-bones.

That of Victorine was even all around, a sign of ponderation; but her brother had an unfortunate cranium—a very large protuberance in the mastoid angle of the parietal bones indicated the organ of destructiveness, of murder; and a swelling farther down was the sign of covetousness, of theft. Bouvard and Pécuchet remained dejected for eight days.

But it was necessary to comprehend the exact sense of words: what we call combativeness implies contempt for death. If it causes homicides, it may, likewise bring about the saving of lives. Acquisitiveness includes the tact of pickpockets and the ardour of merchants. Irreverence has its parallel in the spirit of criticism, craft in circumspection. An instinct always resolves itself into two parts, a bad one and a good one. The one may be destroyed by cultivating the other, and by this system a daring child, far from being a vagabond, may become a general. The sluggish man will have only prudence; the penurious, economy; the extravagant, generosity.

A magnificent dream filled their minds. If they carried to a successful end the education of their pupils, they would later found an establishment having for its object to correct the intellect, to subdue tempers, and to ennoble the heart. Already they talked about subscriptions and about the building.

Their triumph in Ganot's shop had made them famous, and people came to consult them in order that they might tell them their chances of good luck.

All sorts of skulls were examined for this purpose —bowl-shaped, pear-shaped, those rising like sugar

loaves, square heads, high heads, contracted skulls and
flat skulls, with bulls' jaws, birds' faces, and eyes like
pigs'; but such a crowd of people disturbed the hairdresser in his work.   Their elbows rubbed against the
glass cupboard that contained the perfumery, they
put the combs out of order, the wash-hand stand was
broken; so he turned out all the idlers, begging of
Bouvard and Pécuchet to follow them, an ultimatum
which they unmurmuringly accepted, being a little
worn out with cranioscopy.

Next day, as they were passing before the little
garden of the captain, they saw, chatting with him,
Girbal, Coulon, the keeper, and his younger son,
Zephyrin, dressed as an altar-boy. His robe was
quite new, and he was walking below before returning to the sacristy, and they were compliment-
ing him.

Curious to know what they thought of him, Placquevent asked "these gentlemen" to feel his young
man's head.

The skin of his forehead looked tightly drawn;
his nose, thin and very gristly at the tip, drooped
slantwise over his pinched lips; his chin was pointed,
his expression evasive, and his right shoulder was
too high.

"Take off your cap," said his father to him.

Bouvard slipped his hands through his straw-col-
oured hair; then it was Pécuchet's turn, and they
communicated to each other their observations in low
tones:

"Evident *love of books!* Ha! ha! *approbativeness!
Conscientiousness* wanting! No *amativeness!*"

"Well?" said the keeper.

Pécuchet opened his snuff-box, and took a pinch.

"Faith!" replied Bouvard, "this is scarcely a genius."

Placquevent reddened with humiliation.

"All the same, he will do my bidding."

"Oho! Oho!"

"But I am his father, by God! and I have certainly the right——"

"Within certain limits," observed Pécuchet.

Girbal interposed. "The paternal authority is indispensable."

"But if the father is an idiot?"

"No matter," said the captain; "his power is none the less absolute."

"In the interests of the children," added Coulon.

According to Bouvard and Pécuchet, they owed nothing to the authors of their being; and the parents, on the other hand, owed them food, education, forethought—in fact, everything.

Their good neighbours protested against this opinion as immoral. Placquevent was hurt by it as if it were an insult.

"For all that, they are a nice lot that you collect on the high-roads. They will go far. Take care!"

"Care of what?" said Pécuchet sourly.

"Oh! I am not afraid of you."

"Nor I of you either."

Coulon here used his influence to restrain the keeper and induce him to go away quietly.

For some minutes there was silence. Then there was some talk about the dahlias of the captain, who would not let his friends depart till he had exhibited every one of them.

Bouvard and Pécuchet were returning homeward when, a hundred paces in front of them, they noticed Placquevent; and close beside him Zephyrin was lifting up his elbow, like a shield, to save his ear from being boxed.

What they had just heard expressed, in another form, were the opinions of the count; but the example of their pupils proved how much liberty had the advantage over coercion. However, a little discipline was desirable.

Pécuchet nailed up a blackboard in the museum for the purpose of demonstrations. They each resolved to keep a journal wherein the things done by the pupil, noted down every evening, could be read next morning, and, to regulate the work by ringing the bell when it should be finished. Like Dupont de Nemours, they would, at first, make use of the paternal injunction, then of the military injunction, and familiarity in addressing them would be forbidden.

Bouvard tried to teach Victorine ciphering. Sometimes he would make mistakes, and both of them would laugh. Then she would kiss him on the part of his neck which was smoothest and ask leave to go, and he would give his permission.

Pécuchet at the hour for lessons in vain rang the bell and shouted out the military injunction through the window. The brat did not come. His socks were always hanging over his ankles; even at table he thrust his fingers into his nostrils, and did not even keep in his wind. Broussais objects to reprimands on this point on the ground that "it is necessary to obey the promptings of a conservative instinct."

Victorine and he made use of frightful language, saying, *mé itou* instead of *moi aussi, bère* instead of *boire, al* instead of *elle,* and *deventiau* with the *iau;* but, as grammar cannot be understood by children, and as they would learn the use of language by hearing others speak correctly, the two worthy men watched their own words till they found it quite distressing.

They held different views about the way to teach geography. Bouvard thought it more logical to begin with the commune, Pécuchet with the entire world.

With a watering-pot and some sand he sought to demonstrate what was meant by a river, an island, a gulf, and even sacrificed three flower-beds to explain three continents; but the cardinal points could not be got into Victor's head.

On a night in January Pécuchet carried him off in the open country. While they walked along he held forth on astronomy: mariners find it useful on their voyages; without it Christopher Columbus would not have made his discovery. We owe a debt of gratitude to Copernicus, to Galileo, and to Newton.

It was freezing hard, and in the dark blue sky countless stars were scintillating. Pécuchet raised his eyes.

"What! No Ursa Major!"

The last time he had seen it, it was turned to the other side. At length he recognised it, then pointed out the polar star, which is always turned towards the north, and by means of which travellers can find out their exact situation.

Next day he placed an armchair in the middle of the room and began to waltz round it.

"Imagine that this armchair is the sun and that I am the earth; it moves like this."

Victor stared at him, filled with astonishment.

After this he took an orange, passed through it a piece of stick to indicate the poles, then drew a circle across it with charcoal to mark the equator. He next moved the orange round a wax candle, drawing attention to the fact that the various points on the surface were not illuminated at the same time—which causes the difference of climates; and for that of the seasons he sloped the orange, inasmuch as the earth does not stand up straight—which brings about the equinoxes and the solstices.

Victor did not understand a bit of it. He believed that the earth turns around in a long needle, and that the equator is a ring pressing its circumference.

By means of an atlas Pecuchet exhibited Europe to him; but, dazzled by so many lines and colours, he could no longer distinguish the names of different places. The bays and the mountains did not harmonise with the respective nations; the political order confused the physical order. All this, perhaps, might be cleared up by studying history.

It would have been more practical to begin with the village, and go on next to the arrondissement, the department, and the province; but, as Chavignolles had no annals, it was absolutely necessary to stick to universal history. It was rendered embarrassing by such a variety of details that one ought only to select its beautiful features. For Greek history there are: "We shall fight in the shade," the banishment of Aristides by the envious, and the confidence of Alexander in his physician. For Roman, the geese of the Capitol, the tripod of Scævola, the barrel of Regulus. The bed of roses of Guatimozin is noteworthy for America. As for France, it supplies the vase of Soissons, the oak of St. Louis, the death of Joan of Arc, the boiled hen of Bearnais—you have only too extensive a field to select from, not to speak of *À moi d'Auvergne!* and the shipwreck of the *Vengeur*.

Victor confused the men, the centuries, and the countries. Pécuchet, however, was not going to plunge him into subtle considerations, and the mass of facts is a veritable labyrinth. He confined himself to the names of the kings of France. Victor forgot them through not knowing the dates. But, if Dumouchel's system of mnemonics had been insufficient for themselves, what would it be for him! Conclusion: history can be learned only by reading a great deal. He would do this.

Drawing is useful where there are numerous details; and Pécuchet was courageous enough to try to learn it himself from Nature by working at the landscape forthwith. A bookseller at Bayeux sent him paper, india-rubber, pasteboard, pencils, and fixtures, with a view to the works, which, framed and glazed, would adorn the museum.

Out of bed at dawn, they started each with a piece of bread in his pocket, and much time was lost in finding a suitable scene. Pécuchet wished to reproduce what he found under his feet, the extreme horizon, and the clouds, all at the same time; but the backgrounds always got the better of the foregrounds; the river tumbled down from the sky; the shepherd walked over his flock; and a dog asleep looked as if he were hunting. For his part, he gave it up, remembering that he had read this definition:

"Drawing is composed of three things: line, grain, and fine graining, and, furthermore, the powerful touch. But it is only the master who can give the powerful touch."

He rectified the line, assisted in the graining process, watched over the fine graining, and waited for the opportunity of giving the powerful touch. It never arrived, so incomprehensible was the pupil's landscape.

Victorine, who was very lazy, used to yawn over the multiplication table. Mademoiselle Reine showed her how to stitch, and when she was marking linen she lifted her fingers so nicely that Bouvard afterwards had not the heart to torment her with his lesson in ciphering. One of these days they would resume it. No doubt arithmetic and sewing are necessary in a household; but it is cruel, Pécuchet urged, to bring up girls merely with an eye to the husbands they might marry. Not all of them are destined for wedlock; if we wish them later to do without men, we ought to teach them many things.

The sciences can be taught in connection with the commonest objects; for instance, by telling what wine is made of; and when the explanation was given, Victor and Victorine had to repeat it. It was the same with groceries, furniture, illumination; but for them light meant the lamp, and it had nothing in common with the spark of a flint, the flame of a candle, the radiance of the moon.

One day Victorine asked, "How is it that wood burns?" Her masters looked at each other in confusion. The theory of combustion was beyond them.

Another time Bouvard, from the soup to the cheese, kept talking of nutritious elements, and dazed the two youngsters with fibrine, caseine, fat and gluten.

After this, Pécuchet desired to explain to them how the blood is renewed, and he became puzzled over the explanation of circulation.

The dilemma is not an easy one; if you start with facts, the simplest require proofs that are too involved, and by laying down principles first, you begin with the absolute — faith.

How is it to be solved? By combining the two methods of teaching, the rational and the empirical; but a double means towards a single end is the reverse of method. Ah! so much the worse, then.

To initiate them in natural history, they tried some scientific excursions.

"You see," said they, pointing towards an ass, a horse, an ox, "beasts with four feet — they are called quadrupeds. As a rule, birds have feathers, reptiles scales, and butterflies belong to the insect class."

They had a net to catch them with, and Pécuchet, holding the insect up daintily, made them take notice of the four wings, the six claws, the two feelers, and of its bony proboscis, which drinks in the nectar of flowers.

He gathered herbs behind the ditches, mentioned their names, and, when he did not know them, invented them, in order to keep up his prestige. Besides, nomenclature is the least important thing in botany.

He wrote this axiom on the blackboard: "Every plant has leaves, a calyx, and a corolla enclosing an ovary or pericarp, which contains the seed." Then he ordered his pupils to go looking for plants through the fields, and to collect the first that came to hand.

Victor brought him buttercups; Victorine a bunch of strawberries. He searched vainly for the pericarp.

Bouvard, who distrusted his own knowledge, rummaged in the library, and discovered in *Le Redouté des Dames* a sketch of an iris in which the ovaries were not situated in the corolla, but beneath the petals in the stem. In their garden were some scratchweeds and lilies-of-the-valley in flower. These rubiaceæ had no calyx; therefore the principle laid down on the blackboard was false.

"It is an exception," said Pécuchet.

But chance led to the discovery of a field-madder in the grass, and it had a calyx.

"Goodness gracious! If the exceptions themselves are not true, what are we to put any reliance on?"

One day, in one of these excursions, they heard the cries of peacocks, glanced over the wall, and at first did not recognise their own farm. The barn had a slate roof; the railings were new; the pathways had been metalled.

Père Gouy made his appearance.

"'Tisn't possible! Is it you?"

How many sad stories he had to tell of the past three years, amongst others the death of his wife! As for himself, he had always been as strong as an oak.

"Come in a minute."

It was early in April, and in the three fruit-gardens rows of apple trees in full blossom showed their white and red clusters; the sky, which was like blue satin, was perfectly cloudless. Table-cloths, sheets, and napkins hung down, vertically attached to tightly-drawn ropes by wooden pins. Père Gouy lifted them as they passed; and suddenly they came face to face with Madame Bordin, bareheaded, in a dressing-gown, and Marianne offering her armfuls of linen.

"Your servant, gentlemen. Make yourselves at home. As for me, I shall sit down; I am worn out."

The farmer offered to get some refreshment for the entire party.

"Not now," said she; "I am too hot."

Pécuchet consented, and disappeared into the cellar with Père Gouy, Marianne and Victor.

Bouvard sat down on the grass beside Madame Bordin.

He received the annual payment punctually; he had nothing to complain of; and he wished for nothing more.

The bright sunshine lighted up her profile. One of her black head-bands had come loose, and the little curls behind her neck clung to her brown skin, moistened with perspiration. With each breath her bosom heaved. The smell of the grass mingled with the odour of her solid flesh, and Bouvard felt a revival of his attachment, which filled him with joy. Then he complimented her about her property.

She was greatly charmed with it; and she told him about her plans. In order to enlarge the farm-yard, she intended to take down the upper bank.

Victorine was at that moment climbing up the slopes, and gathering primroses, hyacinths, and violets, without being afraid of an old horse that was browsing on the grass at her feet.

"Isn't she pretty?" said Bouvard.

"Yes, she is pretty, for a little girl."

And the widow heaved a sigh, which seemed charged with life-long regret.

"You might have had one yourself."

She hung down her head.

"That depended on you."

"How?"

He gave her such a look that she grew purple, as if at the sensation of a rough caress; but, immediately fanning herself with her pocket-handkerchief:

"You have let the opportunity slip, my dear."

"I don't quite understand." And without rising he drew closer to her.

She remained looking down at him for some time; then smiling, with moist eyes:

"It is your fault."

The sheets, hanging around them, hemmed them in, like the curtains of a bed.

He leaned forward on his elbow, so that his face touched her knees.

"Why?—eh?—why?"

And as she remained silent, while he was in a condition in which words cost nothing, he tried to justify himself; accused himself of folly, of pride.

"Forgive me! Let everything be as it was before. Do you wish it?" And he caught her hand, which she allowed to remain in his.

A sudden gust of wind blew up the sheets, and they saw two peacocks, a male and a female. The female stood motionless, with her tail in the air. The male marched around her, erected his tail into a fan and bridled up, making a clucking noise.

Bouvard was clasping the hand of Madame Bordin. She very quickly loosed herself. Before them, open-mouthed and, as it were, petrified, was young Victor staring at them; a short distance away Victorine, stretched on her back, in the full light of day, was inhaling all the flowers which she had gathered.

The old horse, frightened by the peacocks, broke one of the lines with a kick, got his legs entangled in it, and, galloping through the farmyard, dragged the washed linen after him.

At Madame Bordin's wild screams Marianne rushed up. Pére Gouy abused his horse: "Fool of a beast! Old bag of bones! Infernal thief of a horse!"— kicked him in the belly, and lashed his ears with the handle of a whip.

Bouvard was shocked at seeing the animal maltreated.

The countryman, in answer to his protest, said: "I've a right to do it; he's my own."

This was no justification. And Pécuchet, coming on the scene, added that animals too have their rights, for they have souls like ourselves—if indeed ours have any existence.

"You are an impious man!" exclaimed Madame Bordin.

Three things excited her anger: the necessity for beginning the washing over again, the outrage on her faith, and the fear of having been seen just now in a compromising attitude.

"I thought you were more liberal," said Bouvard.

She replied, in a magisterial manner, "I don't like scamps."

And Gouy laid the blame on them for having injured his horse, whose nostrils were bleeding. He growled in a smothered voice:

"Damned unlucky people! I was going to put him away when they turned up."

The two worthies took themselves off, shrugging their shoulders.

Victor asked them why they had been vexed with Gouy.

"He abuses his strength, which is wrong."

"Why is it wrong?"

Could it be that the children had no idea of justice? Perhaps so.

And the same evening, Pécuchet, with Bouvard sitting at his right, and facing the two pupils with some notes in his hand, began a course of lectures on morality.

"This science teaches us to exercise control over our actions.

"They have two motives — pleasure and interest, and a third, more imperious — duty.

"Duties are divided into two classes: first, duties towards ourselves, which consist in taking care of our bodies, protecting ourselves against all injury." (They understood this perfectly.) "Secondly, duties towards others; that is to say, to be always loyal, good-natured, and even fraternal, the human race being only one single family. A thing often pleases us which is injurious to our fellows; interest is a different thing from good, for good is in itself irreducible." (The children did not comprehend.) He put off the sanction of duties until the next occasion.

In the entire lecture, according to Bouvard, he had not defined "good."

"Why do you wish to define it? We feel it."

So, then, the lessons of morality would suit only moral people — and Pécuchet's course did not go further.

They made their pupils read little tales tending to inspire them with the love of virtue. They plagued Victor to death.

In order to strike his imagination, Pécuchet suspended from the walls of his apartment representations of the lives of the good person and the bad person respectively. The first, Adolphe, embraced his mother, studied German, assisted a blind man, and was admitted into the Polytechnic School. The bad person, Eugène, began by disobeying his father, had a quarrel in a café, beat his wife, fell down dead drunk, smashed a cupboard — and a final picture represented him in jail, where a gentleman, accompanied by a young lad, pointed him out, saying, "You see, my son, the dangers of misconduct."

But for the children, the future had no existence. In vain were their minds saturated with the maxim that "work is honourable," and that "the rich are sometimes unhappy." They had known workmen in no way honoured, and had recollections of the château, where life seemed good. The pangs of remorse were depicted for them with so much exaggeration that they smelled humbug, and after that became distrustful. Attempts were then made to govern their conduct by a sense of honour, the idea of public opinion, and the sentiment of glory, by holding up to their admiration great men; above all, men who made themselves useful, like Belzunce, Franklin, and Jacquard. Victor displayed no longing to resemble them.

One day, when he had done a sum in addition without a mistake, Bouvard sewed to his jacket a ribbon to symbolise the Cross. He strutted about with it; but, when he forgot about the death of Henry IV., Pécuchet put an ass's cap on his head. Victor began to bray with so much violence and for so long a time, that it was found necessary to take off his pasteboard ears.

Like him, his sister showed herself vain of praise, and indifferent to blame.

In order to make them more sensitive, a black cat was given to them, that they might take care of it; and two or three coppers were presented to them, so that they might bestow alms. They thought the requirement unjust; this money belonged to them.

In compliance with the wish of the pedagogues, they called Bouvard "my uncle," and Pécuchet "good friend;" but they "thee'd" and "thou'd" them, and half the lessons were usually lost in disputes.

Victorine ill-treated Marcel, mounted on his back, dragged him by the hair. In order to make game of his hare-lip, she spoke through her nose like him; and the poor fellow did not venture to complain, so fond was he of the little girl. One evening his hoarse voice was unusually raised. Bouvard and Pécuchet went down to the kitchen. The two pupils were staring at the chimneypiece, and Marcel, with clasped hands, was crying out:

"Take him away! It's too much—it's too much!"

The lid of the pot flew off like the bursting of a shell. A greyish mass bounded towards the ceiling, then wriggled about frantically, emitting fearful howls.

They recognised the cat, quite emaciated, with its hair gone, its tail like a piece of string, and its dilated eyes starting out of its head. They were as white as milk, vacant, so to speak, and yet glaring.

The hideous animal continued its howling till it flung itself into the fireplace, disappeared, then rolled back in the middle of the cinders lifeless.

It was Victor who had perpetrated this atrocity; and the two worthy men recoiled, pale with stupefaction and horror. To the reproaches which they addressed to him, he replied, as the keeper had done with reference to his son and the farmer with reference to his horse: "Well! since it's my own," without ceremony and with an air of innocence, in the placidity of a satiated instinct.

The boiling water from the pot was scattered over the floor, and saucepans, tongs, and candlesticks lay everywhere thrown about.

Marcel was some time cleaning up the kitchen, and his masters and he buried the poor cat in the garden under the pagoda.

After this Bouvard and Pécuchet had a long chat about Victor. The paternal blood was showing itself. What were they to do? To give him back to M. de Faverges or to entrust him to others would be an admission of impotence. Perhaps he would reform.

No matter! It was a doubtful hope; and they no longer felt any tenderness towards him. What a pleasure it would have been, however, to have near them a youth interested in their ideas, whose progress they could watch, who would by and by have become a brother to them! But Victor lacked intellect, and heart still more. And Pécuchet sighed, with his hands clasped over his bent knee.

"The sister is not much better," said Bouvard.

He pictured to himself a girl of nearly fifteen years, with a refined nature, a playful humour, adorning the house with the elegant tastes of a young lady; and, as if he had been her father and she had just died, the poor man began to weep.

Then, seeking an excuse for Victor, he quoted Rousseau's opinion: "The child has no responsibility, and cannot be moral or immoral."

Pécuchet's view was that these children had reached the age of discretion, and that they should study some method whereby they could be corrected. Bentham lays down that a punishment, in order to be effectual, should be in proportion to the offence —its natural consequence. The child has broken a pane of glass—a new one will not be put in: let him suffer from cold. If, not being hungry any longer, he asks to be served again, give way to him: a fit of indigestion will quickly make him repent. Suppose he is lazy—let him remain without work: boredom of itself will make him go back to it.

But Victor would not endure cold; his constitution could stand excesses; and doing nothing would agree with him.

They adopted the reverse system: medicinal punishment. Impositions were given to him; he only became more idle. They deprived him of sweet things; his greediness for them redoubled. Perhaps irony might have success with him? On one occasion, when he came to breakfast with dirty hands, Bouvard jeered at him, calling him a " gay cavalier," a "dandy," "yellow gloves." Victor listened with lowering brow, suddenly turned pale, and flung his plate at Bouvard's head; then, wild at having missed him, made a rush at him. It took three men to hold him. He rolled himself on the floor, trying to bite. Pécuchet, at some distance, sprinkled water over him out of a carafe: he immediately calmed down; but for two days he was hoarse. The method had not proved of any use.

They adopted another. At the least symptom of anger, treating him as if he were ill, they put him to bed. Victor was quite contented there, and showed it by singing.

One day he took out of its place in the library an old cocoanut, and was beginning to split it open, when Pécuchet came up:

"My cocoanut!"

It was a memento of Dumouchel! He had brought it from Paris to Chavignolles. He raised his arms in indignation. Victor burst out laughing. "Good friend" could not stand it any longer, and with one good box sent him rolling to the end of the room, then, quivering with emotion, went to complain to Bouvard.

Bouvard rebuked him.

"Are you crazy with your cocoanut? Blows only brutalise; terror enervates. You are disgracing yourself!"

Pécuchet returned that corporal chastisements were sometimes indispensable. Pestalozzi made use of them; and the celebrated Melancthon confesses that without them he would have learned nothing.

His friend observed that cruel punishments, on the other hand, had driven children to suicide. He had in his reading found examples of it.

Victor had barricaded himself in his room.

Bouvard parleyed with him outside the door, and, to make him open it, promised him a plum tart.

From that time he grew worse.

There remained a method extolled by Monseigneur Dupanloup: "the severe look." They tried to impress on their countenances a dreadful expression, and they produced no effect.

"We have no longer any resource but to try religion."

Pécuchet protested. They had banished it from their programme.

But reasoning does not satisfy every want. The heart and the imagination desire something else. The supernatural is for many souls indispensable. So they resolved to send the children to catechism.

Reine offered to conduct them there. She again came to the house, and knew how to make herself liked by her caressing ways.

Victorine suddenly changed, became shy, honey-tongued, knelt down before the Madonna, admired the sacrifice of Abraham, and sneered disdainfully at the name of Protestant.

She said that fasting had been enjoined upon her. They made inquiries: it was not true. On the feast of Corpus Christi some damask violets disappeared from one of the flower-beds to decorate the processional altar: she impudently denied having cut them. At another time she took from Bouvard twenty sous, which she placed at vesper-time in the sacristan's collecting-plate.

They drew from this the conclusion that morality is distinguishable from religion; when it has not another basis, its importance is secondary.

One evening, while they were dining, M. Marescot entered. Victor fled immediately.

The notary, having declined to sit down, told what had brought him there.

Young Touache had beaten — all but killed — his son. As Victor's origin was known, and as he was unpopular, the other brats called him "Convict," and not long since he had given Master Arnold Marescot a drubbing, which was an insult. "Dear Arnold" bore the marks of it on his body.

"His mother is in despair, his clothes are in rags, his health is imperilled. What are we coming to?"

The notary insisted on severe chastisement, and, amongst other things, on Victor being henceforth kept away from catechism, to prevent fresh collisions.

Bouvard and Pécuchet, although wounded by his haughty tone, promised everything he wished — yielded.

Had Victor obeyed a sentiment of honour or of revenge? In any case, he was no coward.

But his brutality frightened them. Music softens manners. Pécuchet conceived the notion of teaching him the solfeggio.

Victor had much difficulty in reading the notes readily and not confounding the terms *adagio, presto*, and *sforzando*. His master strove to explain to him the gamut, perfect harmony, the diatonic, the chromatic, and the two kinds of intervals called major and minor.

He made him stand up straight, with his chest advanced, his shoulders thrown back, his mouth wide open, and, in order to teach by example, gave out intonations in a voice that was out of tune. Victor's voice came forth painfully from his larynx, so contracted was it. When the bar began with a crotchet rest, he started either too soon or too late.

Nevertheless Pécuchet took up an air in two parts. He used a rod as a substitute for a fiddlestick, and moved his arm like a conductor, as if he had an orchestra behind him; but, engaged as he was in two tasks, he sometimes made a mistake; his blunder led to others on the part of the pupil; and, knitting their brows, straining the muscles of their

necks, they went on at random down to the end of
the page.

At length Pécuchet said to Victor:

"You're not likely to shine in a choral society."

And he abandoned the teaching of music.

Besides, perhaps Locke is right: "Music is associated with so much profligate company that it is
better to occupy oneself with something else."

Without desiring to make an author of him, it
would be convenient for Victor to know how to
despatch a letter. A reflection stopped them: the
epistolary style cannot be acquired, for it belongs ex-
clusively to women.

They next thought of cramming his memory with
literary fragments, and, perplexed about making
selections, consulted Madame Campan's work. She
recommends the scene of Eliakim, the choruses in
Esther, and the entire works of Jean Baptiste Rousseau.

These are a little old-fashioned. As for romances,
she prohibits them, as depicting the world under too
favourable colours. However, she permits *Clarissa
Harlowe* and *The Father of a Family,* by Mrs. Opie.*
Who is this Mrs. Opie?

They did not find her name in the Biographie of
Michaud.

There remained fairy tales. "They would be expecting palaces of diamonds," said Pécuchet. Literature develops the intellect, but excites the passions.

Victorine was sent away from catechism on account of her conduct. She had been caught kissing

---

*This is possibly a reference to that once celebrated specimen of
English didactic fiction, *Fathers and Daughters,* by Mrs. Amelia
Opie.— TRANSLATOR.

the notary's son, and Reine made no joke of it: her face looked grave under her cap with its big frills.

After such a scandal, why keep a young girl so corrupted?

Bouvard and Pécuchet called the curé an old fool. His housekeeper defended him, muttering:

"We know you!—we know you!"

They made a sharp rejoinder, and she went off rolling her eyes in a fearful manner.

Victorine was, in fact, smitten with a fancy for Arnold, so nice did she think him, with his embroidered collar, his velvet jacket, and his well-scented hair; and she had been bringing bouquets to him up to the time when Zephyrin told about her.

What foolishness was exhibited regarding this adventure, the two children being perfectly innocent!

The two guardians thought Victor required a stirring amusement like hunting; this would lead to the expense of a gun, of a dog. They thought it better to fatigue him, in order to tame the exuberance of his animal spirits, and went in for coursing in the fields.

The young fellow escaped from them, although they relieved each other. They could do nothing more; and in the evening they had not the strength to hold up the newspaper.

Whilst they were waiting for Victor they talked to the passers-by, and through the sheer necessity of playing the pedagogue, they tried to teach them hygiene, deplored the injuries from floods and the waste of manures, thundered against such superstitions as leaving the skeleton of a blackbird in a barn, putting consecrated wood at the end of a stable and a bag of worms on the big toes of people suffering from fever.

They next took to inspecting wet nurses, and were incensed at their management of babies: some soaked them in gruel, causing them to die of exhaustion; others stuffed them with meat before they were six months old, and so they fell victims to indigestion; several cleaned them with their own spittle; all managed them barbarously.

When they saw over a door an owl that had been crucified, they went into the farmhouse and said:

"You are wrong; these animals live on rats and field-mice. There has been found in a screech-owl's stomach a quantity of caterpillars' larvæ."

The country-folk knew them from having seen them, in the first place, as physicians, then searching for old furniture, and afterwards looking for stones; and they replied:

"Come, now, you pair of play-actors! don't try to teach us."

Their conviction was shaken, for the sparrows cleanse the kitchen-gardens, but eat up the cherries. The owls devour insects, and at the same time bats, which are useful; and, if the moles eat the slugs, they upset the soil. There was one thing of which they were certain: that all game should be destroyed as fatal to agriculture.

One evening, as they were passing along by the wood of Faverges, they found themselves in front of Sorel's house, at the side of the road. Sorel was gesticulating in the presence of three persons. The first was a certain Dauphin, a cobbler, small, thin, and with a sly expression of countenance; the second, Père Aubain, a village porter, wore an old yellow frock-coat, with a pair of coarse blue linen trousers;

the third, Eugéne, a man-servant employed by M. Marescot, was distinguished by his beard cut like that of a magistrate.

Sorel was showing them a noose in copper wire attached to a silk thread, which was held by a clamp — what is called a snare — and he had discovered the cobbler in the act of setting it.

"You are witnesses, are you not?"

Eugène lowered his chin by way of assent, and Père Aubain replied:

"Once you say so."

What enraged Sorel was that anyone should have the audacity to set up a snare at the entrance of his lodge, the rascal imagining that one would have no idea of suspecting it in such a place.

Dauphin adopted the blubbering system:

"I was walking over it; I even tried to break it." They were always accusing him. They had a grudge against him; he was most unlucky.

Sorel, without answering him, had drawn out of his pocket a note-book and a pen and ink, in order to make out an official report.

"Oh, no!" said Pécuchet.

Bouvard added: "Let him go. He is a decent fellow."

"He — a poacher!"

"Well, such things will happen."

And they proceeded to defend poaching: "We know, to start with, that the rabbits nibble at the young sprouts, and that the hares destroy the corn crops — except, perhaps, the woodcock——"

"Let me alone, now." And the gamekeeper went on writing with clenched teeth.

"What obstinacy!" murmured Bouvard.

"Another word, and I shall send for the gendarmes!"

"You are an ill-mannered fellow!" said Pécuchet.

"You are no great things!" retorted Sorel.

Bouvard, forgetting himself, referred to him as a blockhead, a bully; and Eugène kept repeating, "Peace! peace! let us respect the law"; while Père Aubain was groaning three paces away from them on a heap of pebbles.

Disturbed by these voices, all the dogs of the pack rushed out of their kennels. Through the railings their black snouts could be seen, and, rushing hither and thither they kept barking loudly.

"Don't plague me further," cried their master, "or I'll make them go for your breeches!"

The two friends departed, satisfied, however, with having upheld progress and civilisation.

Next day a summons was served on them to appear at the police court for offering insults to the gamekeeper, and to pay a hundred francs' compensation, "reserving an appeal to the public administration, having regard to the contraventions committed by them. Costs: 6 francs 75 centimes.— TIERCELIN, Summoner."

Wherefore a public administration? Their heads became giddy; then, becoming calm, they set about preparing their defence.

On the day named, Bouvard and Pécuchet repaired to the court-house an hour too early. No one was there; chairs and three cushioned seats surrounded an oval table covered with a cloth; a niche had been made in the wall for the purpose of placing a stove there; and the Emperor's bust, which was on a pedestal, overlooked the scene.

They strolled up to the top room of the building, where there was a fire-engine, a number of flags, and in a corner, on the floor, other plaster busts— the great Napoleon without a diadem; Louis XVIII. with epaulets on a dress-coat; Charles X., recognisable by his hanging lip; Louis Philippe, with arched eyebrows and hair dressed in pyramid fashion, the slope of the roof grazing the nape of his neck; and all these objects were befouled by flies and dust. This spectacle had a demoralising effect on Bouvard and Pécuchet. Governing powers excited their pity as they made their way back to the main hall.

There they found Sorel and the field-keeper, the one wearing his badge on his arm, and the other his military cap.

A dozen persons were talking, having been summoned for not having swept in front of their houses, or for having let their dogs go at large, or neglecting to attach lanterns to their carts, or for keeping a public-house open during mass-time.

At length Coulon presented himself, wrapped in a robe of black serge and wearing a round cap with velvet edgings. His clerk sat down at his left, the mayor, scarfed, at his right; and shortly afterwards the case of Sorel against Bouvard and Pécuchet was called.

Louis-Martial-Eugène Lenepveur, valet at Chavignolles (Calvados), availed himself of his character as a witness to unburden himself of all he knew about a great many things that were foreign to the issue.

Nicolas-Juste Aubain, day-labourer, was afraid both of displeasing Sorel and of injuring "these gentlemen." He had heard abusive words, and yet he had his doubts about it. He pleaded that he was deaf.

The justice of the peace made him sit down; then, addressing himself to the gamekeeper: "Do you persist in your declarations?"

"Certainly."

Coulon then asked the two defendants what they had to say.

Bouvard maintained that he had not insulted Sorel, but that in taking the poacher's part he had vindicated the rights of the peasantry. He recalled the abuses of feudal times and the ruinous huntings of the nobles.

"No matter! The contravention——"

"Allow me to stop you," exclaimed Pécuchet.

The words "contravention," "crime," and "delict" were of no value. To seek in this way to class punishable acts was to take an arbitrary basis. As much as to say to citizens: "Don't bother yourself as to the value of your actions; that is determined by the punishment inflicted by authority." However, the penal code appeared to him an absurd production devoid of principles.

"That may be," replied Coulon; and he proceeded to pronounce his judgment.

But here Foureau, who represented the public administration, arose. They had outraged the gamekeeper in the exercise of his functions. If no regard were shown for propriety, everything would be destroyed.

"In short, may it please Monsieur the Justice of the Peace to apply the maximum penalty."

This was ten francs, in the form of damages to Sorel.

"Bravo!" exclaimed Bouvard.

Coulon had not finished.

"Impose on them, in addition, a fine of five francs for having been guilty of the contravention mentioned by the public administration."

Pécuchet turned around to the audience:

"The fine is a trifle to the rich man, but a disaster to the poor man. As for myself, it matters nothing to me."

And he presented the appearance of defying the court.

"Really," said Coulon, "I am astonished that people of intelligence ——"

"The law dispenses you from the possession of it," retorted Pécuchet. "The justice of the peace occupies his post indefinitely, while the judge of the supreme court is reputed capable up to seventy-five years, and the judge of first instance is no longer so at seventy."

But, at a gesture from Foureau, Placquevent advanced.

They protested.

"Ah! if you were appointed by competition!"

"Or by the General Council!"

"Or a committee of experts, and according to a proper list!"

Placquevent moved them on, and they went out while the other defendants' names were being called, believing that they had made a good show in the course of these vile proceedings.

To give vent to their indignation they went that evening to Beljambe's hostelry. His café was empty, the principal customers being in the habit of leaving about ten o'clock. The lamp had been lowered; the walls and the counter seemed shrouded in a fog. A female attendant came on the scene. It was Mélie.

She did not appear agitated, and, smiling, she poured them out two bocks. Pécuchet, ill at ease, quickly left the establishment.

Bouvard came back there alone, entertained some of the villagers with sarcasms at the mayor's expense, and after that went into the smoking-room.

Six months later Dauphin was acquitted for want of evidence. What a shame! These very witnesses who had been believed when testifying against them were now regarded with suspicion. And their anger knew no bounds when the registrar gave them notice to pay the fine. Bouvard attacked the registry as injurious to property.

"You are mistaken," said the collector. "Why, it bears a third of the public expenditure!"

"I would have proceedings with regard to taxes less vexatious, a better system of land registration, alterations in the law as to mortgages, and would abolish the Bank of France, which has the privilege of usury."

Girbal, not being strong on the subject, let the argument fall to the ground, and departed. However, Bouvard made himself agreeable to the innkeeper; he would attract a crowd around him; and, while he was waiting for the guests, he chatted familiarly with the barmaid.

He gave utterance to odd ideas on primary education. On leaving school, pupils ought to be capable of nursing the sick, understanding scientific discoveries, and taking an interest in the arts. The requirements of his programme made him fall out with Petit; and he offended the captain by maintaining that soldiers, instead of losing their time with drilling, would be better occupied in growing vegetables.

When the question of free trade turned up he brought Pécuchet along with him, and the whole winter there were in the café angry looks, contemptuous attitudes, insults and vociferations, with blows of fists on the table that made the beer-glasses jump.

Langlois and the other merchants defended national commerce; Oudot, owner of a spinning factory, and Mathieu, a goldsmith, national industry; the landowners and the farmers, national agriculture: everyone claiming privileges for himself to the detriment of the public at large.

The observations of Bouvard and Pécuchet had an alarming effect.

As they were accused of ignoring the practical side of life, of having a tendency towards levelling, and of immorality, they developed these three ideas: to replace the family name by a registered number; to arrange the French people in a hierarchy, and in such a way that, in order to preserve his grade, it would be necessary for one to submit from time to time to an examination; no more punishments, no more rewards, but in every village an individual chronicle of all persons living there, which would pass on to posterity.

Their system was treated with disdain. They wrote an article about it for the Bayeux daily paper, drew up a note to the prefect, a petition to the Chambers, and a memorial to the Emperor.

The newspaper did not publish their article.

The prefect did not condescend to reply.

The Chambers were silent; and they waited a long time for a communication from the Tuileries.

What, then, was the Emperor occupying his time with?

With women, no doubt.

Foureau, on the part of the sub-prefect, suggested the desirability of more reserve.

They laughed at the sub-prefect, the prefect, the councillors of the prefecture, even the council of state. Administrative justice was a monstrosity, for the administration by means of favours and threats unjustly controls its functionaries. In short, they came to be regarded as a nuisance, and the leading men of the place gave injunctions to Beljambe not to entertain two such fellows.

At this period, Bouvard and Pécuchet were burning to signalise themselves by a work which would dazzle their neighbours; and they saw nothing better than plans for the embellishment of Chavignolles.

Three fourths of the houses should be demolished. They would construct in the centre of the village a monumental square, on the way to Falaise a hospital, slaughter-houses on the way to Caen, and at the "Cows' Pass" a Roman church of many colours.

Pécuchet manufactured a colouring mixture with Indian ink, and did not forget in preparing his plans to give a yellow tint to the woods, a red to the buildings, and a green to the meadows, for the pictures of an ideal Chavignolles pursued him in his daydreams, and he came back to them as he lay on his mattress.

Bouvard was awakened by him one night.

"Are you unwell?"

Pécuchet stammered, "Haussmann prevents me from going to sleep."

About this time he received a letter from Dumouchel to know the cost of sea-baths on the Norman coast.

"Let him go about his business with his baths!
Have we any time to write?"

And, when they had procured a land-surveyor's
chain, a semicircle, a water-level, and a compass, they
began at other studies.

They encroached on private properties. The inhabitants were frequently surprised to see the pair
fixing stakes in the ground for surveying purposes.
Bouvard and Pécuchet announced their plans, and
what would be the outcome of them, with the utmost self-complacency. The people became uneasy,
for, perchance, authority might at length fall in with
these men's views! Sometimes they rudely drove
them away.

Victor scaled the walls and crept up to the roof
to hang up signals there; he exhibited good-will, and
even a degree of enthusiasm.

They were also better satisfied with Victorine.

When she was ironing the linen she hummed in a
sweet voice as she moved her smoothing-iron over the
board, interested herself in looking after the household, and made a cap for Bouvard, with a well-pointed
peak that won compliments for her from Romiche.

This man was one of those tailors who go about
mending clothes in farmhouses. He was taken into
the house for a fortnight.

Hunchbacked, with bloodshot eyes, he made up
for his bodily defects by a facetious disposition.
While the masters were out, he used to amuse Marcel and Victorine by telling them funny stories. He
would put out his tongue as far as his chin, imitate
the cuckoo, or give exhibitions of ventriloquism; and
at night, saving the cost of an inn, he went to sleep
in the bakehouse.

Now, one morning, at a very early hour, Bouvard, being cold, happened to go there to get chips to light his fire.

What he saw petrified him. Behind the remains of the chest, upon a straw mattress, Romiche and Victorine lay asleep together.

He had passed his arm around her waist, and his other hand, long as that of an ape, clutched one of her knees. She was smiling, stretched on her back. Her fair hair hung loose, and the whiteness of the dawn threw its pale light upon the pair.

Bouvard for a moment felt as if he had received a blow in the chest; then a sense of shame prevented him from making a single movement. He was oppressed by painful reflections.

"So young! Lost! lost!" He then went to awaken Pécuchet, and briefly told him everything.

"Ah! the wretch!"

"We cannot help it. Be calm!" And for some time they remained sighing, one after the other—Bouvard, with his coat off and his arms folded; Pécuchet, at the side of his bed, sitting barefooted in a cotton nightcap.

Romiche should leave that very day, when his work was finished. They would pay him in a haughty fashion, and in silence.

But Providence had some spite against them.

Marcel, a short time afterwards, led them to Victor's room and showed them at the bottom of his chest of drawers a twenty-franc piece. The youngster had asked him to get the change of it.

Where did it come from? No doubt it was got by a theft committed while they were going about as engineers. But in order to restore it they would require to know the person; and if some one came to claim it they would look like accomplices.

At length, having sent for Victor, they ordered him to open his drawer : the napoleon was no longer there. He pretended not to understand. A short time before, however, they had seen it, this very coin, and Marcel was incapable of lying. This affair had revolutionised Pécuchet so much that he had, since morning, kept in his pocket a letter for Bouvard :

"Sir,—Fearing lest M. Pécuchet may be ill, I have recourse to your kindness——"

"Whose is the signature, then?"

"Olympe Dumouchel, *née* Charpeau."

She and her husband were anxious to know in which bathing-place—Courseulles, Langrune, or Lucques—the best society was to be found, which was least noisy, and as to the means of transport, the cost of washing, etc.

This importunity made them angry with Dumouchel; then weariness plunged them into deeper despondency.

They went over all the pains that they had taken —so many lessons, precautions, torments!

"And to think that we intended at one time to make Victorine a teacher, and Victor an overseer of works!"

"Ah! how deceived we were in her!"

"If she is vicious, it is not the fault of the lessons she got."

"For my part, to make her virtuous, I would have learned Cartouche's biography."

"Perhaps they needed family life—the care of a mother?"

"I was like one to them," protested Bouvard.

10—7

"Alas!" replied Pécuchet. "But there are natures bereft of moral sense; and education in that case can do nothing."

"Ah! yes, 'tis a fine thing, education!"

As the orphans had not learned any trade, they would seek two situations for them as servants; and then, with the help of God, they would have nothing more to do with them.

And henceforth "My uncle" and "Good friend" made them take their meals in the kitchen.

But soon they grew restless, their minds feeling the need of work, their existence of an aim.

Besides, what does one failure prove? What had proved abortive in the case of children might be more successful with men. And they conceived the idea of preparing a course of lectures for adults.

In order to explain their views, a conference would be necessary. The great hall of the inn would be perfectly suitable for this purpose.

Beljambe, as deputy mayor, was afraid to compromise himself, refused at first, then, thinking that he might make something out of it, changed his mind, and sent word to that effect by his servant-maid.

Bouvard, in the excess of his joy, kissed her on both cheeks.

The mayor was absent. The other deputy, M. Marescot, entirely taken up with his office, would pay little attention to the conference. So it was to take place; and, to the beating of the drum, the hour was announced as three o'clock on the following Sunday.

It was only on the day before that they thought about their costumes. Pécuchet, thank Heaven, had preserved an old ceremonial coat with a velvet collar, two white cravats, and black gloves. Bouvard put on his blue frock-coat, a nankeen waistcoat and beaver shoes; and they were strongly moved when they had passed through the village and arrived at the hostelry of the Golden Cross.

[*Here Gustave Flaubert's manuscript breaks off.*]

[EXTRACT FROM A PLAN FOUND AMONGST GUSTAVE FLAU-
BERT'S PAPERS INDICATING THE CONCLUSION OF THE
WORK.]

CONFERENCE

THE inn of the Golden Cross — two
wooden galleries at the sides on
the first floor, with projecting bal-
cony; main building at the bottom;
café on the ground floor, dining-
room, billiard-room; the doors and
the windows are open.

Crowd: people of rank, ordinary folk.

Bouvard: "The first thing to do is to demonstrate
the utility of our project; our studies entitle us to
pronounce an opinion."

Discourse by Pécuchet of a pedantic description.

Follies of the government and of the administration.
Too much taxation. Two economies to be practised:
the suppression of the religious and of the military
budget.

He is accused of atheism.

"Quite the contrary; but there is need of a religious renovation."

Foureau appears on the scene, and insists on dissolving the meeting.

Bouvard excites a laugh at the mayor's expense by recalling his idiotic bounties for owls. Objection to this.

"If it is necessary to destroy animals that injure plants, it would likewise be necessary to destroy the cattle that devour the grass."

Foureau withdraws.

Discourse by Bouvard — in a familiar style.

Prejudices: celibacy of priests, futility of adultery, emancipation of woman.

"Her earrings are the symbol of her former servitude."

Studs of men.

Bouvard and Pécuchet are reproached with the misconduct of their pupils. Also, why did they adopt the children of a convict?

Theory of rehabilitation. They would dine with Touache.

Foureau, having returned, reads, with a view to having revenge on Bouvard, a petition from him to the municipal council, in which he asks for the establishment of a brothel at Chavignolles. (Contemptuous arguments.)

The meeting is brought to a close amid the utmost confusion.

On their return to their own residence, Bouvard and Pécuchet perceive Foureau's man-servant galloping along the road from Falaise at full speed.

They go to bed, quite jaded, without suspecting how many plots are fermenting against them.—Explain the motives for ill-will towards them actuating the curé, the physician, the mayor, Marescot, the people, everybody.

Next day, at breakfast, they talk about the conference.

Pécuchet sees the future ot humanity in dark colours.

The modern man is lessened, and has become a machine.

Final anarchy of the human race. (Buchner, I., II.)

Impossibility of peace. (*Id.*) Savagery traceable to the excess of individualism and the frenzy of science.

Three hypotheses — first: pantheistic radicalism will break every tie with the past, and an inhuman despotism will result; second: if theistic absolutism triumphs, the liberalism with which humanity has been penetrated since the era of reform succumbs — all is thrown back; third: if the convulsions which have been going on since '89 continue, without an end between the two issues, these oscillations will carry us away by their own force. There will be no longer ideal, religion, morality.

The United States will have conquered the earth.

Future of literature.

Universal greed. There will be no longer anything but a debauch of workmen.

End of the world through the cessation of caloric.

Bouvard sees the future of humanity in a bright light. The modern man is progressive.

Europe will be regenerated by Asia. The historic law that civilisation travels from East to West — the part to be played by China — the two humanities will at length be fused.

Future inventions: modes of travelling. Balloons. Submarine barges with glass windows, in an unchanging calm, the sea's agitation being only on the surface. Passing travellers shall see the fishes and the landscapes in the ocean's depths. Animals tamed. All forms of cultivation.

Future of literature (opposite of industrial literature). Future sciences.— How to regulate the force of magnetism.

Paris will become a winter-garden; fruit will be grown on the boulevards; the Seine filtered and heated; abundance of precious stones artificially made; prodigality as to gilding; lighting of houses — light will be stored up, for there are bodies which possess this property, such as sugar, the flesh of certain molluscs, and the phosphorus of Bologna. People will be ordered to cover the fronts of the houses with a phosphorescent substance, and the radiations from them will illuminate the streets.

Disappearance of evil by the disappearance of want. Philosophy will be a religion.

Communion of all peoples. Public fêtes.

People will travel to the heavenly bodies; and when the earth is used up, humanity will set up housekeeping in the stars.

He has hardly finished when the gendarmes make their appearance. Entry of the gendarmes.

At the sight of them the children are terror-stricken, owing to vague recollections.

Marcel's desolation.

Anxiety on the part of Bouvard and Pécuchet. Do they mean to arrest Victor?

The gendarmes exhibit an order to take them into custody.

It is the conference that brought it on. They are accused of having made attempts on religion, on order, having roused people to revolt, etc.

Sudden arrival of M. and Madame Dumouchel with their baggage; they have come to take sea-baths. Dumouchel is not changed; Madame wears spectacles and composes fables. Their perplexity.

The mayor, knowing that the gendarmes are with Bouvard and Pécuchet, arrives, encouraged by their presence.

Gorju, seeing that authority and public opinion are against them, has thought of profiting by it, and escorts Foureau. Assuming Bouvard to be the richer of the pair, he accuses him of having formerly debauched Mélie.

"I? Never!"

Bouvard breaks into a loud exclamation.

"Let him at least make allowance for the child that is about to be born, for she is pregnant."

This second accusation is based on the liberties taken with her by Bouvard at the café.

The public gradually overrun the house.

Barberou, called into the country by a matter connected with his own business, has just learned at the inn what is going on, and comes on the scene.

He believes Bouvard to be guilty, takes him aside, and makes him promise to yield and give the allowance.

Next comes the doctor, the count, Reine, Madame

Bordin, Madame Marescot, under her umbrella, and other persons of rank.

The village brats, outside the railing, scream out and fling stones into the garden. (It is now well kept, and this makes the inhabitants jealous.)

Foureau wishes to drag Bouvard and Pécuchet to prison.

Barberou interposes, and Marescot, the doctor, and the count likewise interpose with insolent pity.

Explain the order for the arrest. The sub-prefect, on receiving Foureau's letter, has despatched an order to take them into custody, in order to frighten them, together with a letter to Marescot and Faverges, saying that they might be let alone if they exhibited repentance.

Vaucorbeil seeks likewise to defend them.

"'Tis rather to a madhouse that they ought to be sent; they are lunatics. I'll write to the prefect."

Everything is settled. Bouvard will make an allowance for Mélie.

The custody of the children cannot be left to them. They refuse to give them up; but as they have not adopted the orphans according to the forms of law, the mayor takes them back.

They display a revolting insensibility. Bouvard and Pécuchet shed tears at it.

M. and Madame Dumouchel go away.

So everything has gone to pieces in their hands.

They no longer have any interest in life.

A good idea cherished secretly by each of them. They conceal it from each other. From time to time they smile when it comes into their heads; then at last communicate it to each other:

To copy as in former times.

Designing of a bureau with a double desk. (For this purpose they seek the services of a joiner. Gorju, who has heard about their invention, proposes to make it.   Recall the trunk incident.)

Purchase of books, writing materials, sandaracs, erasers, etc.

They sit down to write.

THE DANCE OF DEATH

THE DANCE OF DEATH

(1838)

"Many words for few things!"
"Death ends all ; judgment comes to all."

[This work may be called a prose poem. It is impregnated with the spirit of romanticism, which at the time of writing had a temporary but powerful hold on the mind of Gustave Flaubert.]

DEATH SPEAKS.

AT NIGHT, in winter, when the snow-flakes fall slowly from heaven like great white tears, I raise my voice; its resonance thrills the cypress trees and makes them bud anew.

I pause an instant in my swift course over earth; throw myself down among cold tombs; and, while dark-plumaged birds rise suddenly in terror from my side, while the dead slumber peacefully, while cypress branches droop low o'er my head, while all around me weeps or lies in deep repose, my burning eyes rest on the great white clouds, gigantic winding-sheets, unrolling their slow length across the face of heaven.

How many nights, and years, and ages have I journeyed thus! A witness of the universal birth and of a like decay! Innumerable are the generations I have garnered with my scythe. Like God, I am eternal! The nurse of Earth, I cradle it each night upon a bed both soft and warm. The same recurring feasts; the same unending toil! Each morning I depart, each evening I return, bearing within my mantle's ample folds all that my scythe has gathered. And then I scatter them to the four winds of Heaven!

When high the billows run, when the heavens weep, and shrieking winds lash ocean into madness, then in the turmoil and the tumult do I fling myself upon the surging waves, and lo! the tempest softly cradles me, as in her hammock sways a queen. The foaming waters cool my weary feet, burning from bathing in the falling tears of countless generations that have clung to them in vain endeavour to arrest my steps.

Then, when the storm has ceased, after its roar has calmed me like a lullaby, I bow my head: the hurricane, raging in fury but a moment earlier dies instantly. No longer does it live, but neither do the men, the ships, the navies that lately sailed upon the bosom of the waters.

'Mid all that I have seen and known,—peoples and thrones, loves, glories, sorrows, virtues—what have I ever loved? Nothing—except the mantling shroud that covers me!

My horse! ah, yes! my horse! I love thee too! How thou rushest o'er the world! thy hoofs of steel resounding on the heads bruised by thy speeding feet.

Thy tail is straight and crisp, thine eyes dart flames, the mane upon thy neck flies in the wind, as

on we dash upon our maddened course. Never art thou weary! Never do we rest! Never do we sleep! Thy neighing portends war; thy smoking nostrils spread a pestilence that, mist-like, hovers over earth. Where'er my arrows fly, thou overturnest pyramids and empires, trampling crowns beneath thy hoofs! All men respect thee; nay, adore thee! To invoke thy favour, popes offer thee their triple crowns, and kings their sceptres; peoples, their secret sorrows; poets, their renown. All cringe and kneel before thee, yet thou rushest on over their prostrate forms.

Ah, noble steed! Sole gift from heaven! Thy tendons are of iron, thy head is of bronze. Thou canst pursue thy course for centuries as swiftly as if borne up by eagle's wings; and when, once in a thousand years, resistless hunger comes, thy food is human flesh, thy drink, men's tears. My steed! I love thee as Pale Death alone can love!

Ah! I have lived so long! How many things I know! How many mysteries of the universe are shut within my breast!

Sometimes, after I have hurled a myriad of darts, and, after coursing o'er the world on my pale horse, have gathered many lives, a weariness assails me, and I long to rest.

But on my work must go; my path I must pursue: it leads through infinite space and all the worlds. I sweep away men's plans together with their triumphs, their loves together with their crimes, their very all.

I rend my winding-sheet; a frightful craving tortures me incessantly, as if some serpent stung continually within.

I throw a backward glance, and see the smoke of fiery ruins left behind; the darkness of the night; the agony of the world. I see the graves that are the work of these, my hands; I see the background of the past —'tis nothingness! My weary body, heavy head, and tired feet, sink, seeking rest. My eyes turn towards a glowing horizon, boundless, immense, seeming to grow increasingly in height and depth. I shall devour it, as I have devoured all else.

When, O God! shall I sleep in my turn? When wilt Thou cease creating? When may I, digging my own grave, stretch myself out within my tomb, and, swinging thus upon the world, list the last breath, the death-gasp, of expiring nature?

When that time comes, away my darts and shroud I'll hurl. Then shall I free my horse, and he shall graze upon the grass that grows upon the Pyramids, sleep in the palaces of emperors, drink the last drop of water from the sea, and snuff the odour of the last slow drop of blood! By day, by night, through the countless ages, he shall roam through fields eternal as the fancy takes him; shall leap with one great bound from Atlas to the Himalayas; shall course, in his insolent pride, from heaven to earth; disport himself by caracoling in the dust of crumbled empires; shall speed across the beds of dried-up oceans; shall bound o'er ruins of enormous cities; inhale the void with swelling chest, and roll and stretch at ease.

Then haply, faithful one, weary as I, thou finally shalt seek some precipice from which to cast thyself; shalt halt, panting before the mysterious ocean of infinity; and then, with foaming mouth, dilated nostrils, and extended neck turned towards the horizon, thou shalt, as I, pray for eternal sleep; for repose for thy fiery feet; for a bed of green leaves, whereon reclining thou canst close thy burning eyes forever. There, waiting motionless upon the brink, thou shalt desire a power stronger than thyself to kill thee at a single blow — shalt pray for union with the dying storm, the faded flower, the shrunken corpse. Thou shalt seek sleep, because eternal life is torture, and the tomb is peace.

Why are we here? What hurricane has hurled us into this abyss? What tempest soon shall bear us away towards the forgotten planets whence we came?

Till then, my glorious steed, thou shalt run thy course; thou mayst please thine ear with the crunching of the heads crushed under thy feet. Thy course is long, but courage! Long time hast thou carried me: but longer time still must elapse, and yet we shall not age.

Stars may be quenched, the mountains crumble, the earth finally wear away its diamond axis; but we two, we alone are immortal, for the impalpable lives forever!

But to-day thou canst lie at my feet, and polish thy teeth against the moss-grown tombs, for Satan has abandoned me, and a power unknown compels me to obey his will. Lo! the dead seek to rise from their graves.

Satan, I love thee! Thou alone canst comprehend my joys and my deliriums. But, more fortunate than I, thou wilt some day, when earth shall be no more, recline and sleep within the realms of space.

But I, who have lived so long, have worked so ceaselessly, with only virtuous loves and solemn thoughts,—I must endure immortality. Man has his tomb, and glory its oblivion; the day dies into night, but I—!

And I am doomed to lasting solitude upon my way, strewn with the bones of men and marked by ruins. Angels have fellow-angels; demons their companions of darkness; but I hear only sounds of a clanking scythe, my whistling arrows, and my speeding horse. Always the echo of the surging billows that sweep over and engulf mankind!

SATAN.

Dost thou complain,— thou, the most fortunate creature under heaven? The only, splendid, great, unchangeable, eternal one—like God, who is the only Being that equals thee! Dost thou repine, who some day in thy turn shalt disappear forever, after thou hast crushed the universe beneath thy horse's feet?

When God's work of creating has ceased; when the heavens have disappeared and the stars are quenched; when spirits rise from their retreats and wander in the depths with sighs and groans; then, what unpicturable delight for thee! Then shalt thou sit on the eternal thrones of heaven and of hell—shalt overthrow the planets, stars, and worlds—shalt loose thy steed in fields of emeralds and diamonds—shalt make his litter of the wings torn from the angels,— shalt cover him with the robe of righteousness! Thy saddle shall be broidered with the stars of the empyrean,— and then thou wilt destroy it! After thou hast annihilated everything,— when naught remains but empty space,— thy coffin shattered and thine arrows broken, then make thyself a crown of stone from heaven's highest mount, and cast thyself into the abyss of oblivion. Thy fall may last a million æons, but thou shalt die at last. Because the world must end; all, all must die,—except Satan! Immortal more than God! I live to bring chaos into other worlds!

DEATH.

But thou hast not, as I, this vista of eternal nothingness before thee; thou dost not suffer with this death-like cold, as I.

SATAN.

Nay, but I quiver under fierce and unrelaxing heats of molten lava, which burn the doomed and which e'en I cannot escape.

For thou, at least, hast only to destroy. But I bring birth and I give life. I direct empires and govern the affairs of States and of hearts.

I must be everywhere. The precious metals flow, the diamonds glitter, and men's names resound at my command. I whisper in the ears of women, of poets, and of statesmen, words of love, of glory, of ambition. With Messalina and Nero, at Paris and at Babylon, within the self-same moment do I dwell. Let a new island be discovered, I fly to it ere man can set foot there; though it be but a rock encircled by the sea, I am there in advance of men who will dispute for its possession. I lounge, at the same instant, on a courtesan's couch and on the perfumed beds of emperors. Hatred and envy, pride and wrath, pour from my lips in simultaneous utterance. By night and day I work. While men are burning Christians, I luxuriate voluptuously in baths perfumed with roses; I race in chariots; yield to deep despair; or boast aloud in pride.

At times I have believed that I embodied the whole world, and all that I have seen took place, in verity, within my being.

Sometimes I weary, lose my reason, and indulge in such mad follies that the most worthless of my minions ridicule me while they pity me.

No creature cares for me; nowhere am I loved,— neither in heaven, of which I am a son, nor yet in hell, where I am lord, nor upon earth, where men deem me a god. Naught do I see but paroxysms of rage, rivers of blood, or maddened frenzy. Ne'er shall my eyelids close in slumber, never my spirit find repose, whilst thou, at least, canst rest thy head upon the cool, green freshness of the grave. Yea, I must ever dwell amid the glare of palaces, must listen to the curses of the starving, or inhale the stench of crimes that cry aloud to heaven.

God, whom I hate, has punished me indeed! But my soul is greater even than His wrath; in one deep sigh I could the whole world draw into my breast, where it would burn eternally, even as I.

When, Lord, shall thy great trumpet sound? Then a great harmony shall hover over sea and hill. Ah! would that I could suffer with humanity; their cries and sobs should drown the sound of mine!

[*Innumerable skeletons, riding in chariots, advance at a rapid pace, with cries of joy and triumph. They drag broken branches and crowns of laurel, from which the dried and yellow leaves fall continually in the wind and the dust.*]

Lo, a triumphal throng from Rome, the Eternal City! Her Coliseum and her Capitol are now two grains of sand that served once as a pedestal; but Death has swung his scythe: the monuments have fallen. Behold! At their head comes Nero, pride of my heart, the greatest poet earth has known!

[*Nero advances in a chariot drawn by twelve skeleton horses. With the sceptre in his hand, he strikes the bony backs of his steeds. He stands erect, his shroud flapping behind him in billowy folds. He turns, as if upon a race-course; his eyes are flaming and he cries loudly:*]

NERO.

Quick! Quick! And faster still, until your feet dash fire from the flinty stones and your nostrils fleck your breasts with foam. What! do not the wheels smoke yet? Hear ye the fanfares, whose sound reached even to Ostia; the clapping of the hands, the cries of joy? See how the populace shower saffron on my head! See how my pathway is already damp with sprayed perfume! My chariot whirls on; the pace is swifter than the wind as I shake the golden reins! Faster and faster! The dust clouds rise; my mantle floats upon the breeze, which in my ears sings "Triumph! triumph!" Faster and faster! Hearken to the shouts of joy, list to the stamping feet and the plaudits of the multitude. Jupiter himself looks down on us from heaven. Faster! yea, faster still!

[*Nero's chariot now seems to be drawn by demons; a black cloud of dust and smoke envelops him; in*

*his erratic course he crashes into tombs, and the re-
awakened corpses are crushed under the wheels of
the chariot, which now turns, comes forward, and
stops.*]

NERO.

Now let six hundred of my women dance the
Grecian Dances silently before me, the while I lave
myself with roses in a bath of porphyry. Then let
them circle me, with interlacing arms, that I may
see on all sides alabaster forms in graceful evolution,
swaying like tall reeds bending over an amorous pool.

And I will give the empire and the sea, the Sen-
ate, and Olympus, the Capitol, to her who shall embrace me the most ardently; to her whose heart
shall throb beneath my own; to her who shall
enmesh me in her flowing hair, smile on me sweet-
est, and enfold me in the warmest clasp; to her who
soothing me with songs of love shall waken me to
joy and heights of rapture!

Rome shall be still this night; no barque shall
cleave the waters of the Tiber, since 'tis my wish to
see the mirrored moon on its untroubled face and
hear the voice of woman floating over it. Let perfumed breezes pass through all my draperies! Ah, I
would die, voluptuously intoxicated.

Then, while I eat of some rare meat, that only I
may taste, let some one sing, while damsels, lightly
draped, serve me from plates of gold and watch my
rest. One slave shall cut her sister's throat, because
it is my pleasure — a favourite with the gods — to
mingle the perfume of blood with that of food, and
cries of victims soothe my nerves.

This night I shall burn Rome. The flames shall light up heaven, and Tiber shall roll in waves of fire!

Then, I shall build of aloes wood a stage to float upon the Italian sea, and the Roman populace shall throng thereto chanting my praise. Its draperies shall be of purple, and on it I shall have a bed of eagles' plumage. There I shall sit, and at my side shall be the loveliest woman in the empire, while all the universe applauds the achievements of a god! And though the tempest roar around me, its rage shall be extinguished 'neath my feet, and sounds of music shall o'ercome the clamor of the waves!

What didst thou say? Vindex revolts, my legions fly, my women flee in terror? Silence and tears alone remain, and I hear naught but the rolling of thunder. Must I die, now?

DEATH.

Instantly!

NERO.

Must I give up my days of feasting and delight, my spectacles, my triumphs, my chariots and the applause of multitudes?

DEATH.

All! All!

SATAN.

Haste, Master of the World! One comes — One who will put thee to the sword. An emperor knows how to die!

NERO.

Die! I have scarce begun to live! Oh, what great deeds I should accomplish—deeds that should make Olympus tremble! I would fill up the bed of hoary ocean and speed across it in a triumphal car. I would still live—would see the sun once more, the Tiber, the Campagna, the Circus on the golden sands. Ah! let me live!

DEATH.

I will give thee a mantle for the tomb, and an eternal bed that shall be softer and more peaceful than the Imperial couch.

NERO.

Yet, I am loth to die.

DEATH.

Die, then!

[*He gathers up the shroud, lying beside him on the ground, and bears away Nero, wrapped in its folds.*]

RABELAIS

RABELAIS*

NO NAME in literature has been more generally cited than that of Rabelais; and never, perhaps, has one been cited with so much ignorance and injustice. Thus, to some minds he is merely a drunken, cynical old monk, with a mind disordered and fantastic, as obscene as it is ingenious, dangerous in its ideas and revolting in their expression. To others he is a practical philosopher, gentle and moderate; sceptical, certainly, but, after all, an honest man of reputable life. He has been alternately loved and despised, misunderstood and rehabilitated; and ever since his prodigious genius first launched at the world his biting and all-embracing satire, in the form of the colossal mocking glee of giants, creatures of his imagination, each century has puzzled over his meaning, and has inter-

---

*The manuscript of this essay, unlike all other early manuscripts of Gustave Flaubert, bears no date. It belongs to the earliest of his writing, a time when there was a far from unanimous opinion among the literary *cognoscenti* regarding the work of Rabelais.

preted in a thousand fashions this long enigma, apparently so trivial, gross and merry, but in reality profound and true.

Rabelais' work is a historical achievement, in itself so important that it belongs to and illumines the thought of each age. Thus, at the beginning of the sixteenth century, when first given to the world, it was in reality an open revolt, a moral pamphlet. It had the importance of actuality and the controlling power of a revolution. Rabelais may be regarded as a Luther in his own way. His sphere was that of laughter, but his power over men was such that with titanic mockery he demolished more of evil than the good man of Wittenberg, with all his anger. He managed everything so well — wielded so cleverly the sharp chisel of satire — that his laughter became a terror. His work is the embodiment of the grotesque; it is as eternal as the world.

Rabelais was the father of the frank and naïve literature of the seventeenth century — of Molière and La Fontaine, — all were immortals, geniuses, in spirit the most essentially French of Gallic writers. All three regarded poor human nature with a smile at once good-natured and cynical; all were frank, free and easy in their language, men in every sense of the word: careless of philosophers, of sects, of religions, they were of the religion of mankind itself, and well they understood it. They turned it over, analysed and dissected it; one in a strange story full of gross obscenities, bursting with laughter and blasphemy; the second, on the stage, in deftly constructed dialogue, full of truth and wisdom and a naïveté almost sublime — more of a philosopher in the simple laughter of his Mascarille, in the good sense of Phi-

linte, or in the bilious spleen of Alceste, than any
other philosopher that ever lived; and the third, in
fables for children with morals for men, in verses full
of good-nature and kindly humour, in words and
phrases, wherein rests something of sublimity; in
crystalline sonnets, in all the poetic gems that deck
his name with splendid ornaments.

But Rabelais is to-day a subject of serious study,
the favourite author of those rare minds that rise superior to the ordinary limitations of intelligence. Besides those men whose names we cite, La Bruyère
studied and appreciated his work with the utmost
impartiality. The great romancer was not sufficiently
correct to please the scrupulous taste of Boileau, or
to accord with the reserve and purity of Racine.
That prudish age, governed by Madame de Mainte-
non, so well typified in the flat and angular garden
at Versailles, was ashamed of literature at once so
frank and open, nude and picturesque. This giant
made them fear. They seemed instinctively to feel
that they were placed between two terrible epochs:
the sixteenth century, which produced a Luther and
a Rabelais, and the Revolution, which was to give a
Mirabeau, a Robespierre. First the demolishers of
faith, then the demolishers of life: two abysses', twixt
which they stood firm in the adoration of themselves!

In the eighteenth century things were still worse.
Philosophers then were of a high moral tone, and
would have none of Rabelais. The poor curate of
Meudon would have found himself much out of place
in the salons of the witty and beautiful *marquises,*
or in the intellectual society of Madame du Deffand
or Madame Geoffrin. Never would they have comprehended the flashing darts of wit, the bubbling

spirits, the whirlwind, the poetic mind, throbbing with adventures, inventions, travel, and extravagances. The petty and affected tastes, the cold and formal manners of the age, were horrified at aught that might be called licentiousness of mind. The "Precieuses" probably preferred to have it in their manners! Voltaire, for instance, could pardon Rabelais because he ridiculed the Church; but of his style, of his meaning, Voltaire had scarce an idea, although he claimed to have a key to the great work, which he summed up in vicious epigram: "A mass of the grossest refuse ever vomited by a drunken monk."

It is quite natural that this should have been his opinion. The glory and value of Rabelais, as in the case of all great men, all illustrious names, have long been vigorously disputed. His genius is unique, exceptional; its product stands alone among the histories of the literatures of the world. Where is his rival to be found?

To go back to antiquity, shall we cite Petronius or Apuleius, with their studied and premeditated art, their classic style, their scholarly conceptions?

Passing to the Middle Ages, shall we compare the epics of the twelfth century, the comic and the morality plays? No, certainly not; and although much of the comic material in the work of Rabelais is characteristic of the grotesque humour and manners of the Middle Ages, we do not find its predecessor in any literary document.

Coming down to modern times, his closest imitator, Béroald of Verville, author of *L'Art de Parvenir,* is so far removed from his model in style and power that it is scarcely worth while to make a comparison. Sterne attempted to reproduce the style of Rabelais, but his affectation and over-refined sensibility destroyed the parallel.

No, Rabelais is unique because he himself expresses the traits and characteristics of an entire century. His work possesses the highest significance in literature, politics, morals and religion. Certain geniuses appear from time to time, to create new literatures, or to resuscitate old ones; they deliver their message to the world, express the sentiment of their own generation, and we hear from them no more.

Homer sang the glories of the martial life, of the valiant and warlike youth of the world, the vernal season when the trees put forth new sprouts. In Virgil's day civilisation was already old; we find him full of tears, of shadows, sentiment and delicacy. Dante is sombre and radiant at the same time; he was the Christian poet, the bard of death and of hell, full of melancholy and of hope also. In olden times, if satiety overtook a people, if doubt entered into all hearts, if all beautiful dreams, all illusions, all Utopian yearnings fell, one by one, destroyed by stern realities, by science, reason, and analysis, what did the poet do? He retired within himself; he had sublime flights of pride and enthusiasm, and moments of poignant despair. He sang the agonies of the heart and the vagaries of fancy. Then, all the griefs that compassed him, the sobs that rang in his ears, the maledictions that he heard on every side, resounded in his soul — which God had made great, responsive, all-embracing — and issued thence through the voice of genius, to mark forever in history an epoch in a nation's life, to record its sorrows, and carve indelibly the names of its unfortunates. In our own day Lord

Byron has done this. For this reason, the true poet is more accurate than the historian, and indeed most poets are more strictly truthful than historians. Great writers, then, may be compared, in the realms of thought, to the capitals of kingdoms. They absorb the brains of every province and every individuality; mingling those qualities of each that are distinctively personal and original, they amalgamate them, arrange them, and after a time the result is seen in the form of art.

Rabelais was born in 1483, the year that Louis XI. died. Luther had just become known. The king had overthrown the ancient feudalism; the monks were about to attack the Papacy: this situation describes the history of the Middle Ages — a period divided between the wars of Nations and of the Church. But the people, weary of both, would have no more of either. They realised that the men of arms devoured their substance and ruined them; they knew the priests made use of them for their own selfish purposes, besides deceiving them. For some time the people contented themselves with inscribing satires and scurrilities on the stones of the cathedrals, with making songs against the seigneurs, or publishing, broadcast, biting criticisms of the ruling power or of the nobility, as in the *Romance of the Rose*. But something more was wanted: a revolt, a reform. Symbols were old, and so were mystery plays and poems; and there was a general feeling that an entirely new form of attack was desirable. Science was needed, even in poetry and philosophy.

In 1473, a caricature representing the Church, with the body of a woman, the legs of a chicken, the claws of a vulture, and the tail of a serpent, was cir-

culated throughout Europe. It was the epoch of
Comines, of Machiavelli, of Arétin. The Papacy had
lately had Alexander VI.; now it had Leo X., who
was no better. An intellectual orgy had set in,
destined to be long, and to end with blood. During
the eighteenth century this was repeated, and the
termination was the same.

In the chaotic conditions belonging to this epoch
lived Rabelais. We are not surprised that, in the
midst of this society, corrupt from its debaucheries
and tottering on its foundations, and being witness
to such ruin and devastation, the genius of this wonderful man prompted him to reveal, by means of
withering sarcasm, the frightful past of the Middle
Ages, the effects of which were still felt in his own
century, which looked back upon that past with
horror.

In my opinion, those who have claimed to possess a key to Rabelais, to be able to understand his
allegories, and to translate each jest into its real
significance, do not understand him in the least. His
satire is general and universal, not at all personal or
local. A careful reading of his work should prove
the fallacy of such pretensions.

Shall I cite all that was done in this respect in
the sixteenth century, and tell of all the abuse poured
by that century upon the Middle Ages, of which it
was the outcome? For instance, without saying anything of Ariosto, are not Falstaff, Sancho Panza, and
Gargantua a grotesque trilogy forming a bitter satire
on the old society?

Falstaff belongs wholly to England; he is John
Bull bloated with beer and pork; fat, sensual, running
away from the dead, eternally drawing from his

10—9

pocket a flask of old Spanish wine. He possesses none of the terrible grotesqueness of Iago, or of the deliberate immorality of Schiller's Hassan, the Moor. His greatest passion was self-love; he carried it to the highest degree; it was even sublime. He was egotism personified, with a certain facility in analysis and a strain of ridicule, by which he managed to turn everything to his own advantage.

As for peaceful Sancho Panza, mounted on his lazy, tawny ass, snoring all night and sleeping all day, a poltroon, not able to understand the meaning of heroism, full of proverbs, the prosaic man *par excellence,*— is not his base blood the crying reason why he endeavours with all his power to stop Don Quixote from tilting at the windmills, which the worthy knight takes for giants? The man of gentle birth attacks them, nevertheless, but he breaks his arm and wounds his head. His helmet is a barber's basin, his horse, Rosinante, and a labourer's donkey brays at the sight of his coat-of-arms.

Placed between these two figures, that of Gargantua is vaguer, less precise. His characterisation is ampler, freer, and grander. Gargantua is less gluttonous, less sensual than Falstaff, and not so lazy as Sancho Panza; but he is a greater drinker, a heartier laugher, and makes a louder clamour. He is terrible and monstrous in his gaiety.

One more reflection: the satire of Rabelais does not apply to his own day only. He denounces, for all time, all abuses, crimes, and everything that is ridiculous. Perhaps he was able to foresee a better state of the body politic and a society whose moral laws should be purified. Existing conditions aroused his pity, and, to employ a trivial expression, all the world was a farce. And he made himself a part of the farce.

Since his time, what has been done? Everything has changed. Reform has come, with independence of thought. We have had the Revolution. We possess material independence. And what besides all this?

Thousands of questions have been discussed,— sciences, arts, philosophies, theories,— how many questions even during the last twenty years! What a whirlwind of thoughts and ideas! Where will they lead us?

Let us see. Where are we? Are we in the twilight or in full dawn? We have no more Christianity. What have we? I ask. Railways, factories, chemists, mathematicians. To be sure, our bodies are better off, we suffer less in the flesh, but the heart still bleeds! Do you not feel the perturbation of your soul, although its outward covering seems calm and happy? It is plunged in the abyss of universal scepticism; it is overcome by that deadly ennui that seizes upon our race even in the cradle. Meanwhile, politicians babble, poets have scarcely time to rhyme their fancies and scribble them hastily on ephemeral sheets of paper; and the suicidal bullet is heard in every garret and every palace where dwell misery, pride, or satiety!

Material questions have been settled. But others —have they also been solved? Answer me that! And the longer you delay in filling this yawning chasm in the soul of mankind, the more I mock at your efforts to be happy, and laugh at your miserable sciences, that are worth no more than a blade of grass.

Now is the time for another genius like Rabelais to arise. Let him be without anger, without hatred, without grief. What could he laugh at? Not at kings—there are no more; nor at God, because although we may have lost our faith, yet a certain fear remains; nor at the Jesuits, for they are an old story.

What could he laugh at, then? The material world has improved, or at least it is on the road to improvement.

But the other? He would have fine sport with that. And if such a poet could conceal his tears and laugh instead, I assure you his book would be the most terrible and the most sublime that ever has been written!

Preface to the Last Songs

(POSTHUMOUS POEMS)

OF

LOUIS BOUILHET.

Preface to the Last Songs
(*POSTHUMOUS POEMS*)
OF
LOUIS BOUILHET.

————

T WOULD perhaps make criticism easier, if, before giving our opinion, we should make known our preferences. To omit this preliminary distinction is a great injustice, as every book contains a peculiarity pertaining to the writer himself, which, independently of the execution, will charm or irritate us according to our preferences. We are never completely charmed unless a book appeals to our feelings and our intellect at the same time.

First, let us discuss the object of the book. "Why this novel, this drama? Of what use is it? etc." Instead of following the author's idea, instead of pointing out to him where he failed of his aim, and how he should have gone about to attain it, we bicker with him on a thousand things outside of his subject, always declaring the contrary of what he meant to express. If a critic's sphere extends beyond the author's province, he should first of all look to the æsthetics and the moral.

It is impossible for me to warrant either of these concerning the poet in questions. As for writing his life, it has been linked so closely with mine, that I shall be brief on this subject; individual memoirs belong only to great men. Besides, has not research been exhausted? History will soon absorb all literature. In studying too closely what makes up the author's atmosphere, we fail to give the originality of his genius due consideration. In La Harpe's time, when a masterpiece appeared, we were convinced,— thanks to certain rules!—that it was under no obligation whatsoever; whereas now, after we have examined everything about it, we still wish to discover its right to exist.

I have another scruple. I do not wish to betray the modesty that my friend constantly maintained. At an epoch when insignificant mediocrity aspired to fame, when typography was the medium of all affectations, and the rivalry of the most insipid personalities became a public pest, he was proud of being modest. His photograph was never displayed on the boulevards. No article, no letter, not a single line from him, was ever published in the papers. He did not even belong to the academy of his province. Yet no life is more deserving of praise than his. He lived nobly and labouriously. Though poor, he remained free. He was as strong as a blacksmith, mild as a child, intellectual without being paradoxical, noble without affectation; and those who knew him well will say that I have not praised him enough.

Louis Hyacinthe Bouilhet was born at Cany (Seine Inférieure), the 27th day of May, 1822. His father, chief of ambulances in the campaign of 1812, swam the Bérésina, carrying on his head the regiment's chest, and died quite young from wounds received. His maternal grandfather, Pierre Hourcastremé, dabbled in legislation, poetry, and geometry, received congratulations from Voltaire, corresponded with Turgot and Condorcet, spent nearly all his money buying shells, produced *Les Aventures de Messire Anselme,* an *Essai sur la Faculté de Penser, Les Etrennes de Mnémosyne,* etc., and after being a lawyer in Pau, a journalist in Paris, administrator of the navy at Havre, and a schoolmaster at Montvilliers, died almost a centenarian, bequeathing to his grandson the memory of a strange but charming old man, who powdered his hair, wore knee-breeches and cultivated tulips.

The child was sent to Ingouville, to a boarding-school on a high cliff, and went to the college of Rouen at twelve, where he was usually at the head of his class. He was not a model pupil, however; this term applies to mediocre natures and a calmness of spirit which was rare in those days.

I do not know what students admire nowadays, but our dreams were wildly imaginative. The most enthusiastic dreamt of violent courtships, with gondolas, and fainting ladies carried away in stage-coaches by masked ruffians. Some, more gloomily disposed (admirers of Armand Carrel, a countryman), preferred the clash of the press and the court-room, or the glory of conspiracy. A rhetorician wrote an *Apologie de Robespierre,* which reached a certain gentleman and so scandalised him that it brought on an exchange of notes, followed by a challenge to a duel, in which the said gentleman did not play a very creditable part. One good-natured fellow always wore a red cap; another swore to live as a Mohican; one of my intimate friends aspired to the honour of serving under Abd-el-Kader. Apart from being troubadours, insurgents and Orientals, we were, above all, artists. After studies, we wrote, and read novels till late in the night. Bar . . . , declaring he was tired of life, shot himself; and And . . . hanged himself with his cravat. We certainly deserved little praise for our follies; but we hated platitudes; our minds soared towards noble things. How we revered the masters! How we admired Victor Hugo!

Among this group was Bouilhet, the elegist, the poet of moonlight and ruins. When he was nearly twenty, this affectation disappeared, to give place to a virulent democracy, so genuine that he was about to join a secret society.

He received his bachelor's degree, and was told to choose a profession. He chose medicine, settled his small income on his mother, and taught for a living. His life became painfully labourious; he combined the duties of poet, tutor and saw-bones. Two years later, he was appointed interne at l'Hôtel Dieu in Rouen, under my father's orders. As he could not attend during the day, his turn came oftener than others for night watch. He did not mind it, however, as he had no other time in which to write. All his poems of love, flowers and birds were written in those winter nights, amidst the sick and suffering, or on Sundays in summer, while the patients walked under his window. Those years of sadness were not useless; the contemplation of suffering humanity, the dressing of wounds, the dissecting-table, gave him a better knowledge of mankind. Some would have given way under the strain, the disgust, the torture of having to follow a vocation unsuited to him; but, thanks to his physical and mental health, he stood it cheerfully. Some still remember meeting in the streets of his native city, this handsome though somewhat timid youth, with flowing blond hair, who always carried a note-book, in which he wrote his verses as they came to him; sometimes while teaching, at a friend's house, in a café, during an operation, anywhere. Poor in worldly wealth, but rich in hope, he gave them away. He was a real poet in the classical sense of the word.

When we met again after four years' separation, he read to me three of his plays. The first, entitled *Le Deluge*, described a lover clinging to his beloved, while he watched with anguish the ruins of the fast disappearing world : "Hark to the crashing of the palm-trees on the heights, and to the agonizing cries of Earth!" It was somewhat prolix, and too emphatic, but was replete with force and passion. The second, a satire against the Jesuits, was more resolute and in an entirely different style : "Smile, priests of the boudoir and gather poor feminine souls in your golden nets!" "Charming ministers in the confessional, inflicting penance with love-words on their lips! Heroes of the Gospel, impleading the Lord with flowery language, and treading each day, holy martyrs! on soft carpets the *via crucis!*" "These merchants, at the foot of the cross, casting lots and dividing, piece by piece, O Lord, Thy robe and Thy cloak! These fakirs of holy relics, selling, oh, wonder! Thy heart as amulets, and phials of Thy blood."

We must not forget the disturbances of the times, and must remember that the author was only twenty-two. The play was dated 1844.

The third was an invective to "An author who sold his poems":

> Why seek a famished passion to revive?
> After thy rustic love through green fields strive
> On flowery banks beside the rosy stream
> Archangel, drink to drunkenness the sunny beam,
> Under the willows chant etotic dreams,
> Though Brutus' sins upon thy shoulders weigh
> Doubtless thy simple soul and heart inveigh
> Against the Destiny that took from thee.

"'Tis the greedy Plutus, with his purse full, who quotes smiling, human honesty!"

"Destiny is the bag full of gold into which we plunge our greedy hands with rapture! It is corruption which flaunts before our eyes its alluring breast! It is fear, the silent spectre that disturbs the coward in the hour of danger!"

"Your prudent Apollo, no doubt, passed through the stock exchange to reach the Parnassus? We often see, in the political sky, the morning sun die out before night. Look through your telescope, do you not see Guizot waning and Thiers coming to light? Do you base your changeable faith and your flexible probity on the mobility of the weather?"

"Avaunt! Greek, whose servile words lauded Xerxes the night before Thermopylæ!" He continued in the same rough tone against the administration. He sent his play to the *Reforme,* hoping they would print it; but they refused peremptorily, not wishing to expose themselves to a law suit — for mere literature.

It was near the end of 1845, when my father died, that Bouilhet gave up the practice of medicine. But he continued to teach, and, with the aid of a partner, obtained bachelorships for their pupils. The events of 1848 disturbed his republican faith. He now became a confirmed *littérateur,* fond of metaphors and comparisons, but indifferent to all else.

His thorough knowledge of Latin (he wrote as fluently in Latin as in French) inspired the few Roman sketches, as in *Festons et Astragales* and the poem *Melœnis,* published in the *Revue de Paris,* on the eve of a political crisis. The moment was badly chosen. The public's fancy and courage were considerably cooled, and it was not disposed, neither were the powers, to accept independent genius; besides, individual style always seems insurrectionary to governments and immoral to commoners. The exaltation of vulgarism, the banishment of poetry, became more than ever the rage. Wishing to show good judgment, they rushed headlong into stupidity; anything above the ordinary bored them.

As a protest, he took refuge in forgotten places and in the far East; and thence came the *Fossiles* and different Chinese plays.

However, the provincial atmosphere stifled him; he needed a vaster field; and severing his connections, he came to Paris; but at a certain age one can no longer acquire the Parisian judgment; the things that seem simple to a native of the boulevards, are impracticable to a man of thirty-three arriving in the great city, having few acquaintances and no income, and unaccustomed to solitude. Then his bad days began.

His first book, *Madame de Montarcy,* received on approval at the Theatre Français, and refused at the second reading, lingered for two years and was only accepted at the Odéon in November, 1856. The first performance was a rousing success. The applause often interrupted the action of the play; a whiff of youth permeated the atmosphere; it was a reminiscence of 1830. That night he became known; his success was assured. He could have collaborated, and made money with his name; but he preferred the quietness of Mantes, and went to live in a little house near an old tower, at the turn of the bridge, where his friends visited him on Sundays.

As soon as his plays were written, he took them to Paris; but the whims and fancies of the managers, the critics, the belated appointments, and the loss of time, caused him much weariness. He did not know that art, in a question of art, held such a trifling place! When he joined a committee against the unfair dealings at the Theatre Français, he was the only member that did not complain of the rates of authors' royalties.

With what pleasure he returned to his daily distraction, the study of Chinese! He pursued it ten years, merely as a study of the race, intending to write a grand poem on the Celestial Empire. Days when his heart was too full, he relieved himself by writing lyrical verses on the restrictions of the stage. His luck had turned, but with the *Conjuration d'Ambroise* it returned, and it lasted all winter.

Six months later he was appointed conservator of the municipal library of Rouen; and his old dream of leisure and fortune was realized at last! But soon afterward a dullness seized him — the exhaustion from too long a struggle. To counteract this he resumed the Greek tragic style and rapidly composed his last play, *Mademoiselle Aïssé,* which he never corrected. An incurable disease, long neglected, was the cause of his death, which took place on the 18th of July,

1869. He passed away without pain, in the presence
of a friend of his youth and her child, whom he
loved as if he were his own son. Their affection had
increased towards the last, but two other persons
marred their happiness. It seems that in a poet's
family there are always bitter disappointments. An-
noying quarrels, honeyed sarcasms, direct insults to
art, the million and one things that make your heart
bleed,—nothing was spared him while he lived, and
these things followed him to his death-bed.

His fellow-countrymen flocked to his funeral as if
he had been a public man; even the less educated
knowing full well that a superior intellect had passed
away. The whole Parisian press joined in this universal sorrow; even the most hostile expressed their
regrets; a Catholic writer alone spoke disparagingly.
No doubt the connoisseurs in verse deplore the loss of
such a poetical spirit; but those in whom he confided,
who knew his powerful spirit, who benefited by his
advice, they alone know to what height he might
have risen.

He left, besides *Aïssé*, three comedies in prose, a
fairy-scene, and the first act of *Pélerinage de Saint-
Jacques,* a drama in verse, in ten tableaux. He had
outlined two short poems: *Le Bœuf,* depicting the
rustic life of Latium; and *Le Dernier Banquet,* describ-
ing the Roman patricians poisoning themselves at a
banquet the night the soldiers of Alaric are entering
Rome. He wished also to write a novel on the heathen
of the fifth century, the counterpart of the *Martyrs;*
but above all, he desired to write his Chinese tale, the
scenes of which are completely laid out. It was his
supreme ambition to recapitulate modern science, to
write the *De natura rerum* of our age!

Who has the right to classify the talents of his contemporaries, and, thinking himself superior to all, say: "This one comes first, that one second, and this other third"? Fame's sudden changes are numerous. There are irretrievable failures; some long, obscure periods, and some triumphant reappearances. Was not Ronsard forgotten before Sainte-Beuve? In days gone by, Saint-Amant was considered inferior as a poet to Jacques Delille. *Don Quixote, Gil Blas, Manon Lescaut, La Cousine Bette* and other masterpieces, have never had the success of *Uncle Tom*. In my youth, I heard comparisons made between Casimir Delavigne and Victor Hugo, and it seems that "our great national poet" was declining. Let us then be careful, or posterity will misjudge us—perhaps laugh at our bitterness—still more, perhaps, at our adulations; for the fame of an author does not spring from public approbation, but from the verdict of a few intellects, who, in the course of time, impose it upon the public.

Some will say that I have given my friend too high a place; but they know not, no more do I, what place he will retain. Because his first book is written in stanzas of six lines each, with triple rhymes, like *Naouma,* and begins like this: "Of all the men that ever walked through Rome, in Grecian buskins and linen toga, from Suburra to the Capitoline hill, the handsomest was Paulus," somewhat similar to this: "Of all the libertines in Paris, the first, oldest and most prolific in vice, where debauchery is so easily found, the lewdest of all was Jacques Rolla," without more ado, and ignoring the dissimilarity of execution, poetry, and nature, it was declared that the author of *Melænis* imitated Alfred de Musset! He was condemned on the spot; a farce—it is so easy to label a thing so as to be able to put it aside.

I do not wish to be unfair; but where has Musset, in any part of his works, harmonized description, dialogue, and intrigue in more than two thousand consecutive rhymes, with such results of composition, such choice of language, in short, where is there a work of such magnitude? What wonderful ability was needed to reproduce Roman society, without affectation, yet keeping within the narrow confines of a dramatic fable!

If you look for the primitive idea, the general element in Louis Bouilhet's poems, you will find a kind of naturalism that reminds you of the Renaissance. His hatred of commonplace saved him from platitudes; his inclination towards the heroic was tempered by his wit—he was very witty. This part of his talent was almost unknown; he kept it somewhat in the shadow, thinking it of no consequence; but now nothing hinders me from acknowledging that he excelled in epigrams, sonnets, rondeaux and other jests, written for distraction or pastime, and also through sheer good-nature. I discovered some official speeches for functionaries, New-Year verses for a little girl, some stanzas for a barber, for the christening of a bell, for the visit of a king. He dedicated to one of our friends, wounded in 1848, an ode on the patron of *The Taking of Namur,* where emphasis reached the pinnacle of dullness. To another who killed a viper with his whip he sent a piece entitled: *The struggle of a monster and a genius,* which contained enough imperfect metaphors and ridiculous periphrasis to serve as a model or as a scarecrow. But his best was a masterpiece, in Béranger's style, entitled *The Nightcap!*

His intimate friends will always remember it. It praised glory, the ladies, and philosophy so highly,— it was enough to make all the members of the Caveau burst with the desire of emulating him.

He had the gift of being entertaining—a rare thing for a poet. Compare his Chinese with his Roman plays, *Neera* with *Lied Norman*, *Pastel* with *Clair de Lune*, *Chronique de Printemps* with *Sombre Eglogue*, *Le Navire* with *Une Soirée*, and you will see how productive and ingenious he was.

He has dramatised all human passions; he has written about the mummies, the triumphs of the unknown, the sadness of the stones, has unearthed worlds, described barbaric peoples and biblical scenes, and written lullabies. The scope of his imagination is sufficiently proven in *Les Fossiles*, which Theophile Gautier called "the most difficult subject ever attempted by any poet!" I may add that it is the only scientific poem in all French literature that is really poetical. The stanzas at the end, on the future man, show how well he understood the most transcendent utopias. Among religious works, his *Colombe* will perhaps live as the declaration of faith of the nineteenth century. His individuality manifests itself plainly in *Dernière Nuit*, *A Une Femme*, *Quand vous m'avez quitté*, *Boudeuse*, etc., where he is by turns dismal and ironical; whereas in *La fleur rouge* it bursts out in a singularly sharp and almost savage manner.

He does not look for effect; follows no school but his own individual style, which is versatile, fluent, violent, full of imagination and always musical. He possesses all the secrets of poetry; that is the reason that his works abound with good lines, good all the way through, as in *Le Lutrin* and *Les Châtiments*.

Take, for instance: "Is long like a crocodile, with bird-like extremities." "A big, brown bear, wearing a golden helmet." "He was a muleteer from Capua." "The sky was as blue as a calm sea." "The thousand things one sees when mingling with a crowd."

And this one of the Virgin Mary: "Forever pale from carrying her God."

In one sense of the word, he is classical. His *l'Oncle Million* is written in the most excellent French. "A poem! Make rhymes! It is insanity! I have seen saner men put into a padded cell! Zounds! Who speaks in rhymes? What a farce! Am I imaginative? Do I make verses? Do you know, my boy, what I have had to endure to give you the extreme pleasure of watching, lyre in hand, which way the winds blow? Wisely considered, these frivolities are well enough at odd moments. I myself knew a clerk that wrote verses."

Then further: "I say Léon is not even a poet! He a poet, come! You are joking. Why, I saw him when he was no higher than that! What has he out of the ordinary? He is a rattle-brained, stupid fool, and I warrant you he will be a business man, or I will know the reason why!"

This style goes straight to the point. The meaning comes out so clearly that the words are forgotten; that is, while clinging to it, they do not impede or alter its purport.

But you will say these accomplishments are of no use for the stage; that he was not a successful playwright. The sixty-eight performances of *Montarcy*, ninety of *Hélène Peyron*, and five hundred of *La Conjuration d'Ambroise*, prove the contrary. One must really know what is suitable for the stage, and, above all things, acknowledge that the dominant question is spontaneous and lucrative success. The most experienced are at sea, not being able to follow the vagaries of public taste. In olden times, one went to the theatre to hear beautiful thoughts put into beautiful language. In 1830, furious and roaring passion was the rage; later, such rapidity of action, that the heroes had not time to speak; then, thesis; after that, witty sallies; and now the reproduction of stupid vulgarism appears to monopolize the public favour.

Bouilhet cared nothing for thesis; he hated insipid phrases, and considered what is called "realism" a monstrosity. Stunning effects not being acquired by mild colouring, he preferred bold descriptions, violent situations—that is what made his poems really tragic. His plots weakened sometimes towards the middle, but, for a play in verse, were it more concise, it would crowd out all poetry. *La Conjuration d'Ambroise* and *Mademoiselle Aïssé* show some progress in this respect; but I am not blind; I censure his Louis XIV. in *Madame de Montarcy* as too unreal; in *l'Oncle Million* the feigned illness of the notary; in *Hélène Peyron* the too prolix scene in the fourth act, and in *Dolorès* the lack of harmony between vagueness and precision. In short, his personages are too poetical. He knew how to bring out sensational effects, however. For instance, the reappearance of Marcelline at Dubret's, the entrance of Dom Pedro in the third act of *Dolorès*, the Countess of Brissot in the dungeon, the commander in the last act of *Aïssé*, and the ghostly reappearance of Cassius before the Empress Faustine. This book was unjustly criticised; nor was the atticism understood in *l'Oncle*

Million, it being perhaps the best written of all his plays, as *Faustine* is the most labouriously contrived. They are all very pathetic at the end, filled with exquisite things and real passion. How well suited to the voice his poems are! How virile his words, which make one shiver! Their impulsion resembles the flap of a great bird's wings!

The heroic style of his dramas secured them an enthusiastic reception; but his triumphs did not turn his head, as he knew that the best part of a work is not always understood, and he might owe his success to the weaker. If he had written the same plays in prose, perhaps his dramatic talent would have been extolled; but, unfortunately, he used a medium that is generally disliked. "No comedy in verse!" was the first cry, and later, "No verses on the stage!" Why not confess that we desire none at all?

He never wrote prose; rhymes were his natural dialect. He thought in rhymes, and he loved them so that he read all sorts with equal attention. When we love a thing we love every part of it. Play goers love the green-room; gourmands love to smell cooking; mothers love to bathe their children. Disillusion is a sign of weakness. Beware of the fastidious, for they are usually powerless!

Art, he thought, was a serious thing, its aim being to create a vague exaltation; that alone being its morality. From a memorandum I take the following notes:

"In poetry, one need not consider whether the morals are good, but whether they adapt themselves to the person described; thus will it describe with equal indifference good and bad actions, without suggesting the latter as an example."— PIERRE CORNEILLE.

"Art, in its creations, must strive to please only those who have the right to judge it; otherwise it will follow the wrong path."—GOETHE.

"All the intellectual beauties and details of a tale (if it is well written) are so many useful facts, and are perhaps more precious to the public mind than the main points that make up the subject."—BUFFON.

Therefore art, being its own motive, must not be considered an expedient. No matter how much genius we might use in the development of a story used as an example, another might prove the contrary. A climax is not a conclusion. We must not infer generalities from one particular case; those who think themselves progressive in doing so are working against modern science, which demands that we gather all the facts before proclaiming a law.

Bouilhet did not like that moralising art which teaches and corrects; he liked still less the frivolous art, which strives to divert the mind or stir the feelings; he did not follow democratic art, being convinced that, to be accessible to all, it must descend to the lowest level; as, at this civilised period, when we try to be artless we become silly. As to official art, he refused all its advantages, not wishing to defend causes that are so short-lived.

He avoided paradoxes, oddities, and all deviations; he followed a straight road; that is, the generous feelings, the immutable side of the human soul. As "thoughts are the foundation of language," he tried to think well so as to write well. Although he wrote emotional dramas, he never said: "If Margot wept, the melodrama is good," as he did not believe in replacing emotion by trickery. He hated the new maxim that says, "One must write as one speaks."

It is true, the old way of wasting time in making researches, the trouble taken when bringing out a book, would seem ridiculous nowadays; we are above all those things, we overflow with fluency and genius!

Not that he lacked genius, however; he often made corrections while a rehearsal was in progress. Inspiration, he held, cannot be made, but must come naturally. He followed Buffon's advice, expressing each thought by an image, and made his conceptions as vivid as possible; but the *bourgeois* declared that "atmosphere" was too material a thing to express sentiment; and fearing their sound French judgment might be disturbed and carried beyond its limits, they exclaimed "too much metaphor"! — as if they had any to spare!

Few authors take such pains in choosing their words, in phrasing. He did not give the title of author to those who possess only certain elements of style. Many of the most praised would have been unable to combine analysis, description, and dialogue!

He loved rhythm, in verse as well as in prose. He considered that language without rhythm was tedious, and unfit to stand the test of being read aloud. He was very liberal; Shakespeare and Boileau were equally admired by him; he read Rabelais continually, loved Corneille and La Fontaine, and, although very romantic, he praised Voltaire. In Greek literature, he preferred first of all the Odyssey, then Aristophanes; in Latin, Tacitus and Juvenal. He had also studied Apuleius a great deal.

He despised public speeches, whether addressed to God or to the people; the bigot's style, as that of the labourer; all things that reek of the sewer or of cheap perfume. Many things were unknown to him; such as the fanaticism of the seventeenth century, the infatuation for Calvin, the continuous lamentations on the decline of the arts. He cared little for M. de Maistre, nor did Prudhon dazzle him. In his estimation, sober minds were nothing else than inferior minds; he hated affected good taste, thinking it more execrable than bad; and all discussions on the arts, the gossip of the critics. He would rather have died than write a preface. The following page, taken from a note-book and entitled *Notes et Projets*, will give a better idea: "This century is essentially pedagogic. There is no scribbler, no book, be they never so paltry, that does not press itself upon the public; as to form, it is outlawed. If you happen to write well, you are accused of lacking ideas. Heavens! One must be stupid indeed to want for ideas at the price they bring! By simply using these three words future, progress, society, no matter who you are, you are a poet. How easy to encourage the fools and console the envious! Mediocre, profitable poetry, school-room literature, æsthetic prattle, economical refuse, scrofulous products of an exhausted nation, oh! how I detest you all from the bottom of my heart! You are not gangrene, you are putrescence!"

The day after his death Théophile Gautier wrote: "He carried with pride the old tattered banner, which had seen so many battles; we can make a shroud of it, the valiant followers of Hernani are no more." How true! He devoted his entire life to ideals, loving literature for itself; as the last fanatic loves a religion nearly or quite extinct.

"Second-rate genius," you will say; but fourth-rate ones are not so plentiful now! We are getting

wide of the mark. We are so engrossed in stupidity
and vulgarism that we shun delicacy and loftiness of
mind; we think it a bore to show respect to great
men. Perhaps we shall lose, with literary tradition,
that ethereal element which represented life as more
sublime than it really is; but if we wish our works to
live after us, we must not sneer at fame. By cultivating the mind we acquire some wit. Witnessing
beautiful actions makes us more noble.

If there should be somewhere two young men
who spend their Sundays reading poetry together,
telling each other what they have written and what
they would like to write, and, while indifferent to all
else, conceal this passion from all eyes — if so, my
advice to them is this:

Go side by side, through the woods, reciting
poetry; mingle your souls with the sap of the trees
and the eternity of God's creations; abandon yourselves to reverie and the torpors of sublimity! Give
up your youth to the Muse; it will replace all other
loves. When you have experienced the world's mis-
eries; when everything, including your own existence,
seems to point towards one purpose; when you are
ready for any sacrifice, any test, — then, publish your
works. After that, no matter what happens, you will
look on the wretchedness of your rivals without indignation, and on their success without envy. As
the less favoured will be consoled by the other's success, the one with a stouter heart will encourage the
weaker one; each will contribute his particular gift;
this mutual help will avert pride and delay declina-
tion.

When one of you dies — as we must all die — let
the other treasure his memory; let him use it as a

bulwark against weakness, or, better, as a private altar where he can open his heart and pour out his grief. Many times, in the stillness of night, will he look vainly for his friend's shadow, ready to question him: "Am I doing right? What must I do? Answer me!"—and if this memory be a constant reminder of his sorrow, it will at least be a companion in his solitude.

LETTER TO THE
MUNICIPALITY OF ROUEN
ON THE SUBJECT OF A MEMORIAL
TO
LOUIS BOUILHET.

Letter to the Municipality of Rouen

GENTLEMEN:—

BY A majority of two votes—thirteen votes against eleven (including that of the mayor and his six clerks)—you refused the offer I made you to erect *free of cost,* at any place you might choose in your city, a small fountain ornamented with the bust of Louis Bouilhet.

As I am spokesman for the persons who contributed their money for this purpose, I must protest in their name against this decision—that is, I must reply to the objections uttered in your meeting of the 8th of December last, an account of which appeared in the newspapers of Rouen on the 18th of the same month.

The four principal objections were:

1.— That the subscription committee changed the destination of the monument;

2.— That the municipal budget would be imperilled;

3.— That Bouilhet was not born in Rouen;

4.— That his literary talent is inadequate.

First objection (I use the words as they were printed): "Can the committee modify the intention

and substitute a fountain for a tombstone? Will all
the subscribers accept the substitution?"

We have modified nothing, gentlemen! the monument (a vague expression, not precisely designating
a tombstone) was suggested by M. Ernest Leroy,
ex-prefect of the "Seine-Inférieure," on the day of
Bouilhet's funeral.

I immediately started a subscription, on which
figured the names of an imperial highness, George
Sand, Alexandre Dumas, the great Russian author
Tourgeneff, Harrisse, a New York journalist, etc.
Some subscribers from the *Comedie Française* are:
Mmes. Plessy, Favart, Brohan and M. Bressant; from
the Opéra, M. Faure and Mlle. Nilsson; in short,
after six months, we had about 14,000 francs at our
disposal; besides this, the marble was to be given to
us by the *Beaux-Arts* administration, and the sculptor
chosen by us refused to accept any remuneration.

Surely, all those people, known or unknown, did
not give their time, talent, or money, for the erection
in a cemetery (which very few would ever visit) of
so costly a tombstone; one of those grotesque con-
structions that are adverse to all religious feeling,
to all philosophies, whose derisive pride insults eternity!

No, gentlemen, what they desired was something
less useful—and more moral: that when passing Bouilhet's statue each one could say: "There was a man who,
in this avaricious century, devoted his whole life to
the worship of literature. This mark of respect is
but justice to him, and I have contributed my share
to this reparation." This was their idea; nothing
else. Besides, how do you know? Who asked you
to defend them?

The municipal council say: "As we understand it to be a tombstone, we will give ten metres of ground and subscribe 500 francs." As this decision implies a recrimination, let them keep their 500 francs! As to the ground, we are willing to buy it. What is your price? But enough on your first objection.

The second is dictated by excessive caution: "If the subscription committee have made a mistake in their estimate, the city could not leave it (the monument) unfinished; and we must even now foresee that, if need be, we should have to make up the deficit."

Our estimate was submitted to your architect; as to our funds, if they had been insufficient, rest assured the committee would have made an appeal to the subscribers, or rather, would have supplied them out of their own pockets. Thank heaven! we are rich enough to keep our word! Your excessive anxiety seems somewhat rude.

Third objection: "Bouilhet was not born in Rouen!" Yet, M. Decorde says in his report: "He is one of us"; and after the first performance of *La Conjuration d'Ambroise*, M. Verdrel, ex-Mayor of Rouen, at a banquet given in honor of Bouilhet, complimented him in the most flattering terms; calling him "one of the geniuses of Rouen." For some years, it was quite a fad of the smaller Parisian publications to ridicule the enthusiasm of the people of Rouen for Bouilhet. In the *Charivari*, a caricature represented the people of Rouen offering their respects to *Hélène Peyron* in the shape of bonbons and cakes; in another, I was represented dragging the "Rouenese float."

But no matter. According to you, gentlemen, if an illustrious man is born in a village consisting of thirty shanties, the monument must be erected in that village, and not in the county seat? Then why not erect it in the street, house, or even room where he was born? Suppose his birthplace were unknown (history is not always decisive on this point),—what would you do? Nothing. Am I right?

Fourth objection:—"His literary merit!"

I find in the report many big words on this subject: "Propriety"; "principles." "It must be risky." "It would be a great distinction; an extreme honour; a supreme homage; which must be granted only with extreme caution"; lastly, "Rouen is too large a pedestal for his genius!" Really, such praise was not bestowed even upon the excellent M. Pottier, "whose services to the city library were more conspicuous" (no doubt, because it was your library). Nor, secondly, on Hyacinthe Langlois! I knew him, gentlemen, better than all of you. Do not revive this painful recollection! Never speak of this noble man! His life was a disgrace to his countrymen! You call him "a great Norman celebrity," and, dispensing fame in fantastic manner, you quote among the celebrities of which our city can boast (you can, but do not always) Pierre Corneille! Corneille a celebrity? Really, you are severe! Then, in the same breath, you mention Boieldieu, Lemonnier, Fontenelle, and, gentlemen, you forget Gericault, the dean of modern painting; Saint-Amant, the great poet; Boisgilbert, the first economist of France; De La Salle, who discovered the mouth of the Mississippi; Louis Poterat, inventor of porcelain in Europe,—and others!

That your predecessors should have forgotten to pay high, immoderate, sufficient tribute, or even no tribute at all, to these "celebrities" (Samuel Bochart, for instance, whose name adorns one of the streets of Caen) is an indisputable fact! But does a previous injustice authorise subsequent wrongs?

It is true, nothing has been erected to the memory of Rabelais, Montaigne, Ronsard, Pascal, La Bruyère, Le Sage, Diderot, Vauvenargues, Lamennais, Alexandre Dumas, and Balzac, in their native cities. On the other hand, there is a statue of General de Saint-Pol at Nogent-le-Rotrou; one of General Blanmont at Gisors; one of General Leclerc at Pontoise; one of General Valhubert at Avranches; one of M. Vaisse at Lyons; one of M. Billault at Nantes; one of M. de Morny at Deauville; one of Ancelot at Havre; one of Ponsard at Valence; in a public park at Vire, an enormous bust of Chênedollé; at Séez, in front of the cathedral, a magnificent statue of Conté, etc.

This is all well enough, if the public purse has not suffered. Let those who desire fame pay for it; let those who wish to pay tributes to others, do so at their own cost. This is exactly what we wished to do.

So long as you were subject to no financial risks, your duty was to demand of us a guaranty of execution. Besides the right to choose the spot for our fountain, you had that of rejecting our sculptor and choosing one yourselves. But you are too engrossed in the hypothetical success of *Mademoiselle Aïssé!* "If this drama is not a success, might not the erection of a public monument to his literary talent [Bouilhet's] be looked upon with disfavour?"

M. Nion (who has special charge of the fine arts) thinks that if by chance this drama should be a failure, the adoption of the proposed plan would be

10—11

"rashness" on the part of the municipal council.
So, it would seem that the bone of contention is
the financial success of the piece! If it is a success,
Bouilhet is a great man; if a failure, he is not! What
a noble theory! The immediate success of a drama
has nothing to do with its literary value.   There are
numerous examples: Moliere's *L'Avare* ran four
nights; Racine's *Athalie* and Rossini's *Barbier de
Seville* were hooted.   But rest easy, *Mademoiselle
Aïssé* was a great success.   It does not seem to matter to M. Decorde, your reporter, who says: 'Bouilhet's talent is not proof against criticism'; and: 'His
reputation is not sufficiently established.'   M. Nion
says: 'His method is more remarkable than his
scenic conceptions!   He is not original, not a first-
class author!"   M. Decorde calls him 'an imitator of
Alfred de Musset, who was sometimes successful'!
Really, my dear sir, you are not as indulgent as you
should be towards a contemporary,— you who, artfully
scoffing at this very city of Rouen, whose literary
morals you defend so well, have stigmatized Saint-
Tard as 'a progressive borough.'*   A nice little place,
where, "Despite the city toll, against which they
grumble, liquor-shops and cafés flourish."

If you had been asked for money, I should have
understood your reluctance.

"Here is another thing; we are continually taxed
for the least reason."   'Tis true the bourgeois of Saint-
Tard are not much given to generosity!

We expected better of you after your treatment
of modern slang in your epistle *Des importations*

---

* Read at a public meeting of the Academy of Rouen, Aug. 7th,
1867.

Anglaises * in which are these lines: "I read in a paper that at Boulogne-sur-Mer a fashionable cricket-club had arranged a match. And having so poorly aped fashion, can lay claim to admiration." Attractive lines, but these are better: "I have read somewhere that a miser of Rennes, knowing no better way to avoid giving presents, had died on the New Year."

You are really versatile — whether you praise photograph collections: "It is a pleasant pastime, and everyone has a large collection," or Saint-Ouen Park: "Your fate is that of the great stream once so sought after, and you in your turn are deserted." † Or dancing: "As everything must follow the fashion, Terpsichore has submitted to the law of exchange. Ignoring prohibition, the Lancers have already reached us from Albion." ‡ Or dinners in town: "You must not expect me to divulge what the menu consists of; but from the beginning the dessert adorns the table. Alas! those pleasures are not had for nothing; a winter in the city is more costly than one thinks!" § Or the marvels of modern industry: "And now, thanks to special trains, we can visit Belgium or Switzerland in eight days, and at much less cost. And when De Lesseps has at last made a passage through the Suez Canal, the tourist can take a pleasure trip to India or

---

* Read at the Academy of Rouen, at a public meeting, Aug. 7th, 1865. (See analytical summary of the works of the Academy of Rouen.)

† Letter of condolence to Saint-Ouen park.— Meeting of June 2, 1865. (See analytical summary of the Academy of Rouen.)

‡ Winter in the city. (Letter.— Meeting of Aug. 6th, 1863.)

§ Winter in the city. (Letter.— Meeting Aug. 6th, 1863.)

the extreme Orient as easily as travelling through France." *

Do not stop, by any means! Write dramas even, you who have such a keen conception of dramatic form! And rest assured, honourable sir, that if your "reputation were sufficiently established," and although like Louis Bouilhet's, your "talent" is not "proof against criticism," you are not "original" not "a first-class author," you will never be called "an imitator," even "sometimes successful," of Alfred de Musset!

Besides, your memory is at fault on this point. Did not one of your colleagues of the Academy of Rouen, at the meeting of Aug. 7th, 1862, praise Louis Bouilhet in flattering terms? He praised him so highly as a dramatic author, and denied so energetically that he was an imitator of Alfred de Musset, that when I wrote the preface to *Dernières Chansons*, I simply copied the words of my old friend, Alfred Nion, brother of M. Emile Nion, the gentleman that lacked boldness!

What was the gentleman "who has special charge of the fine arts" afraid of? Of obstructing your public by-ways? Poets like this one (begging your pardon) are not precisely innumerable. Since you have refused to accept his statue, *notwithstanding* our gift of a fountain, you have lost one of your colleagues, M. Thubeuf. I do not wish to speak unbecomingly, or to insult a sorrowful family I have not the honour of knowing, but it seems to me that Nicholas-Louis-Juste Thubeuf is at the present moment as forgotten as if he never had existed, while Bouilhet's name is known over all Europe. *Aïssé*

---

* Vacations. (Familiar letter.— Meeting of Aug. 6th, 1861.)

is being played in St. Petersburg and London. His plays and verses will be printed in six, twenty, even a hundred years hence, and perhaps beyond that. A man is seldom remembered unless he has been amusing or serviceable. You are not able to be the former; grant us the latter. Instead of devoting your time to literary criticism, a pastime that is beyond your powers, attend to more serious things such as: the construction of a bridge; the construction of a bonded-warehouse; the widening of the Rue du Grand-Pont; the opening of a street, running from the Court-House to the docks; the much delayed completion of the spire of the cathedral, etc. Queer collection, indeed! It might be called "Museum of deferred projects."

You are so afraid of compromising yourselves, so afraid to act, that each outgoing administration hands its caution down to its successor. You think caution such a virtue that it would be a crime for you to act. Mediocrity is not detrimental, you think, but one must avoid being enterprising. When the public clamours, a committee is at once appointed; and from that time nothing is done. "We can do absolutely nothing; we await the committee's decision." Invincible argument to soothe public impatience!

Sometimes, however, you are bold enough to act; but it almost creates a scandal: as when the ex-Rue de l'Imperatrice, now the Rue Jeanne-Darc, and the Square Solferino were opened in Rouen. Still: "Public parks are the style now, and Rouen must have one!"*

---

* M. Decorde's poetry. (Letter of condolence to Saint-Ouen Park, already cited.)

But the most important, though the most neglected, of all your projects is the distribution of water throughout the city. Take Saint-Sever, for example, where there is great need of it. What we proposed was, to erect, at any street corner, a small fountain adorned with a statue. Several of you had formally promised that our fountain should be erected; we were therefore greatly surprised at your decision, inasmuch as you are sometimes generous in these matters. The statue to Napoleon I. on the Place Saint-Ouen is an instance. You gave, for the erection of this masterpiece, which had cost 160,000 francs or thereabouts, the small sum of 30,000 francs! The council had appropriated the first time 10,000 francs; the second time, 8,000; and the third time, 5,000, as indemnity to the sculptor, because his *maquette* had casually been overthrown by the committee — always the committee! What aptitude for art! For the statue of Pierre Corneille, proposed in 1805 and erected twenty-nine years later, 1834, you spent 7,037.38 francs — not a cent more. True, he was a great poet, and you are so considerate that you prefer to deprive yourselves of a necessity, rather than honour a second-rate poet!

Permit me to ask two questions: If this fountain, this useful public monument which we offered, had represented anything but Louis Bouilhet's bust, would you have refused it? If it had been intended for one of the capitalists of our district, whose fortune runs into the millions, would you have refused it? I doubt it.

Be careful, or you will be accused of despising those who cannot boast of a fortune! For such cautious men, who consider success the main object, you have sadly erred, gentlemen! The *Moniteur Universel*, *l'Ordre*, the *Paris-Journal*, the *Bien Public*, the *XIXème Siecle*, *l'Opinion Nationale*, the *Constitutionnel*, the *Gaulois*, the *Figaro*, in fact, nearly all the papers, were against you. To convince you, we will simply quote a few lines from the dean of modern critics, Jules Janin:

"When the time came for definitive compensation, the last hope of Louis Bouilhet's friends was dashed to the ground; they encountered all sorts of obstacles. His statue was refused a place in a city that his fame had made illustrious! His friends proposed in vain to erect a much needed fountain, so that the statue ornamenting it might not be thought the main object of this good deed. But how can unjust men understand the cruelty of such a refusal? They might erect a statue to war, but to a poet, never!"

Of the twenty-four composing the committee, eleven sided with us; and Messrs. Vaucquier du Traversin, F. Deschamps and Raoul Duval spoke eloquently in our favour. This affair is trifling in itself, but it may be noted as a characteristic feature of the century — of your class.

"I address myself to you no longer, gentlemen, but to all the *bourgeoisie*. Therefore I say: Conservators who conserve nothing, it is time to follow a different path. You speak of decentralizing, regenerating, — if so, rouse yourselves. Be active! Originate! French nobles lost their prestige for having had, during two centuries, the feelings of menials. The end of the *bourgeois* is at hand, because their feelings are those of the rabble. I do not see that they read different papers, or hear different music, or that their pleasures are more refined. In one as in the other, it is the same love of money; the same wish to destroy idols; the same hatred of superior minds; the same meanness; the same crass ignorance.

Of the seven hundred members of l'Assemblée Nationale, how many are there who could name six kings of France, who know the first rudiments of political economy, who have even read Bastiat? The whole municipality of Rouen, who disowned a poet's talent, no doubt are ignorant of the rules of versification. They do not need to know them, so long as they do not meddle with poetry.

To be respected by those beneath us, we must respect those above us! Before educating the rabble, educate yourselves! Enlightened people, enlighten yourselves! Because of your disdain for superiority, you think you have abundant good sense, you are positive, you are practical. One is never really practical unless he carries it a little farther. . . . You would not enjoy the benefits of industry if your ancestors of the eighteenth century had had other ideals than common usefulness. How we scoffed at Germany—at her dreamers, her ideologists, her ethereal poets! Our milliards compensated her for the time well employed in perfecting plans. It seems to me, it was the dreamer Fichte who reorganized the Prussian army after Jena; and that the poet Koërner sent a few Uhlans against us about 1813!

You practical? Come! You cannot even hold a pen or a gun! You let convicts rob, imprison, and slaughter you! You have lost even the brute's instinct of defence; and when not only your life, but your purse (which ought to be dearer to you), is in danger, you lack the energy to drop a ballot into a box! With all your capital, all your wisdom, you never can form an association equal to *l'Internationale!* All your intellectual efforts consist of trembling for the future. Think! Hasten! or France, between a hideous demagogy and a stupid *bourgeoisie,* will sink lower and lower!

GUSTAVE FLAUBERT.

SELECTED

CORRESPONDENCE

OF

GUSTAVE FLAUBERT

WITH AN

INTIMATE STUDY OF THE AUTHOR

BY

CAROLINE COMMANVILLE

SIMON P. MAGEE
PUBLISHER
CHICAGO, ILL.

INTIMATE REMEMBRANCES

OF

GUSTAVE FLAUBERT

I.

THESE pages are not a biography of Gustave Flaubert, they are simply recollections; my own and those I have collected.

My uncle's life was passed entirely in the intimacy of the family, between his mother and me; to relate the story of this life is to make him better known, more loved and esteemed; in this way I believe that I am fulfilling a pious duty towards his memory.

Before Gustave Flaubert's birth, my grandparents had had three children. The eldest, Achilles, was nine years older than Gustave, and the two other little ones were dead. Then came Gustave and another boy who died in a few months; and finally my mother, Caroline, the last child.

She and her younger brother loved each other with a peculiar tenderness. With but three years difference in their ages, the two little ones were scarcely ever separated from each other. Gustave repeated everything he learned to his sister; she was his pupil, and one of his greatest pleasures was initiating her into literary composition. Later, when he was in Paris, it was to her he wrote; through her was the daily news transmitted to their parents, because that sweet communion had not been lost.

I should say that the greater part of the facts relative to my uncle's infancy have been told me by the old nurse who brought him up and who died three years after him, in 1883. The familiarity permitted with a child was followed in her case by a respect and worship for her master. She was "full of him," recalling his least action, his least word. When she said "Monsieur Gustave," she believed that she was speaking of an extraordinary being. Those who knew him will appreciate the verity contained in the admiration of this old servant.

Gustave Flaubert was four years old when Julie came to Rouen into my grand-parents' service, in 1825. She came from the village of Fleury-on-the-Andelle, situated in that pretty, smiling valley which extends from Pont-Saint-Pierre to the great market-town of Lyons-la-Forêt. The coast of the "Two Lovers" protected its entrance; here and there was a château, sometimes surrounded by water and having its drawbridge, again the superb estate of Radepont, the ruins of an old abbey and the woods of the surrounding hills.

This charming country is fertile in old stories of love and of ghosts. Julie knew them all. She was a skilful story-teller, this simple girl of the people, and endowed with a naturally fine and agreeable mind. Her ancestors, from father to son, had been postilions, rather bad fellows, and hard drinkers.

While Gustave was small he would sit beside her for whole days. In order to amuse him, Julie would join together all the legends she had heard around the fire with those she had read, and, having been kept in bed a year with a bad knee, she had read more than most women of her class.

The child was of a tranquil nature, meditative, possessing an ingenuousness of which he retained traces during his whole life. My grandmother has told me that he would remain for hours with a finger in his mouth, absorbed, and with an almost stupid appearance. When he was six years old an old domestic, called Pierre, used to amuse himself with that innocence; he would say to little Gustave, if he teased for anything, "Go now and look at the end of the garden, or in the kitchen and see whether I am there." And the child would go and say to the cook: "Pierre sent me to see whether he were here." He could not comprehend that they were deceiving him, and while they laughed, would stand thinking, trying to see through the mystery.

My grandmother had taught her oldest son to read, and, wishing to do as much for the second, put herself to the task. The little Caroline, beside Gustave, learned by degrees that she could not keep up with him, and he, being forced to understand this from signs of which no one said anything to him, began to weep large tears. He was, however, eager for knowledge, and his brain worked continually.

Opposite the hospital, in a modest little house in the Rue de Lecat, lived two old people, Father and Mother Mignot. They had an extreme tenderness for their little neighbour. Times without number, the child would open the heavy door of the Hôtel-Dieu, and run across to Father Mignot's knee, upon a signal from him. And it was not the good woman's strawberries that tempted him, but the stories the old man told him. He knew a great many pretty tales of one kind and another, and with what patience he related them! From this time Julie was supplanted. The child was not difficult to please, but had insistent preferences; those that he liked must be told him over and over again.

Father Mignot also read to him. *Don Quixote* especially pleased my uncle; he would never let it be taken from him. And he retained for Cervantes the same admiration all his life.

In the scenes brought about by the difficulty of learning to read, the last irrefutable argument with him was: "Why should I learn, since Papa Mignot can read to me?"

But the age for entering school arrived. He must know once for all that his old friend could not follow him there. Gustave put himself resolutely to work, and at the end of a few months had caught up with the children of his age. He entered the eighth class.

He was not what one would call a brilliant pupil. Continually failing to observe some rule, and not troubling himself to understand his professors, punishments abounded, and the first prize escaped him, except in history, in which he was always first. In philosophy he distinguished himself, but he never comprehended mathematics.

Generous and full of exuberance, he had some warm friends whom he amused extremely by his unquenchable enthusiasm and good humour. His melancholy times, for he had them even then, he passed in a region of his mind accessible to himself alone, and not yet did he show them in his exterior life. He had a great memory, forgetting nothing, neither benevolences nor vexation of which he was the subject. Thus, he preserved for his professor in history, Cheruel, a profound remembrance, and hated a certain usher who had hindered him from reading his favourite book during the study hour.

But his years at the college were miserable; he never could become accustomed to things there, having a horror of discipline, and of everything that savoured of militarism. The custom of announcing the change of exercises by the beating of drums irritated him, and that of filing the pupils in rank when they passed from one class to another exasperated him. Constraint in his movements was a punishment, and his walk with the procession every Thursday was never a pleasure; not that he was feeble, but he had a natural antipathy for all that seemed to him useless motion. His antipathy for walking lasted his whole life. Of all exercises for the body, swimming alone pleased him; he was a very good swimmer.

The dull, labourious days of school life were enlivened by outings on Thursdays and Sundays. Then he saw his beloved family and his little sister, which was a joy unequalled.

In the dormitory during the week, thanks to some hidden pieces of candle, he read some of Victor Hugo's dramas, and his passion for the theatre was kept warm. From the age of ten, Gustave composed tragedies. These pieces, of which he was scarcely able to write the lines, were played by him and his comrades. A great billiard hall opening from the salon was given up to them. The billiard table,

10—12

pushed to one end of the room, served as a stage, which they mounted by means of a crock from the garden. Caroline had charge of the decorations and costumes. His mother's wardrobe was plundered for old shawls, which made excellent peplums. He wrote to one of his principal actors, Ernest Chevalier: "Victory! victory! victory! victory! You will come, and Amédée, Edmond, Madame Chevalier, Mamma, two servants and perhaps some pupils, will be here to see us play. We shall give four pieces that you do not know. But you will soon learn them. The tickets of the first, second, and third classes are made. There will be some armchairs. There will also be scenery and decorations; the curtain is arranged. Perhaps there will be ten or twelve persons. So we must have courage and not fear," etc.

Alfred Le Poittevin, some years older than Gustave, and his sister Laura, were also a part of these representations. The family of Poittevin was bound to that of Flaubert through the two mothers, who had known each other from nine years of age at the *pension*. Alfred Le Poittevin had a very great influence upon my uncle in his youth, contributing to his literary development. He was endowed with a brilliant mind, full of life and eccentricity. He died young, which was a great grief. My uncle speaks of him in his preface to the *Last Songs*.

A few words about my grandparents and upon the moral and intellectual development of my uncle.

My grandfather, whose traits have been sketched in *Madame Bovary*, under those of Doctor Larivière, called in consultation to the bed of the dying Emma, was the son of a veterinary of Nogent-on-the-Seine.

The situation of the family was modest: nevertheless, by denying themselves, they sent their son to Paris to study medicine. He took the first prize in the great competition and by this success was received as a doctor free of further cost. Scarcely had he passed his examinations when he was sent from Dupuytren, where he was house physician, to Rouen to Doctor Laumonier, who was then surgeon of the hospital. This sojourn was supposed to be only temporary, to restore his health, which had become enfeebled from overwork and a life of privation. But, instead of remaining for a few months, the young physician spent all his life there. The frequent appeals of his numerous friends, or the hope of arriving at a high place in the medical profession in Paris, which his successful beginning had justified, never decided him to leave his hospital and a people to whom he became profoundly attached.

But in the beginning, it was love which extended this sojourn,—love for a young girl, a child of thirteen years, a goddaughter of Madame Laumonier, an orphan in a boarding-school, who came each week to visit her godmother.

Anne-Justine-Caroline Fleuriot was born in 1794 at Pont-l'Evêque in Calvados. Through her mother she was allied to the oldest families in Lower Normandy. "A great noise is made," said Charlotte Corday in one of her letters, "about an unequal marriage between Charlotte Cambremer de Croixmare and Jean-Baptiste Francois-Prosper Fleuriot, a doctor without reputation." At thirty years of age Mademoiselle de Croixmare had been sent back to the convent. But the obstacles were finally conquered, the walls of the convent broken and the marriage took place. One year later a daughter was born, and the mother died in giving her birth.

The child, left in the arms of its father, became for him an object of tenderness and worship. At sixteen, my grandmother still remembered with emotion her father's kisses. "He would undress me each evening," she said, "and put me in my bed, wishing to take my mother's place." These paternal cares soon ceased. Doctor Fleuriot, seeing that he was about to die, gave his daughter in charge of two old ladies of Saint-Cyr who had a little school at Honfleur. These ladies promised to keep her until her marriage, but they, too, soon disappeared. Then her tutor, Monsieur Thouret, sent the young girl to Madame Laumonier, sister of Jacques-Guillaume Thouret, Deputy from Rouen to the States-General and President of that Assembly. She came at the same time as my grandfather, when they happened to see each other. Some months later they avowed their love and promised themselves to each another.

The Laumonier household, like many others of that epoch, tolerated, under a spiritual and gracious exterior, a certain lightness of morals. The eminently serious nature of my grandmother and her love preserved her from the dangers of such surroundings. Besides, my grandfather, more far-seeing than she could be, wished her to remain in the boarding-school until she was married. She was eighteen and he twenty-seven at the time of their marriage. Their purse was slender, but their hearts had little fear. My grandfather's portion was in his future; my grandmother had a little farm which brought her a revenue of four thousand francs.

The household was established in the Rue du

Petit-Salut, near the Rue Grand-Pont, a little street of narrow houses, touching one another, where the sun could never penetrate. In my childhood my grandmother would often take me through there, and, looking at the windows, would say in a grave voice, almost religious: "Look, my child, the best years of my life were passed there."

Descended from a Champenois and a Norman, Gustave Flaubert had the characteristic signs of both races; his temperament was very expansive and, at the same time, it was enveloped in the vague melancholy of the people of the north. He was of even temper and gay, sometimes with a touch of buffoonery; but ever at the bottom of his nature was an undefined sadness, a kind of disquiet. He was physically robust, enjoying full, strong pleasures; but his soul, aspiring to an unattainable ideal, suffered without ceasing in not finding it. This applied to the smallest things; because, as a seeker after the exquisite, he had found that the most frequently recurring sentiment was nearly always one of grief. This without doubt added to the sensibility of his nervous system, which the violent commotions of a certain malady (to the paroxysms of which he had had many relapses, especially in his youth) had refined to an extreme point. That came also from his great love of the ideal. This nervous malady threw a veil over his whole life; it was a permanent fear obscuring even his happiest days. However, it had no influence upon his robust health, and the incessant and vigorous work of his brain continued without interruption.

Gustave Flaubert was something of a fanatic; he had taken art for his god, and like a devotee, he knew all the tortures and all the intoxications of the love to which he had sacrificed himself. After hours passed in communion with abstract form, the mystic became man again, was a *bon vivant,* laughed with a frank laugh, put a charming gaiety into the recital of a story, or some pleasant personal remembrance. One of his greatest pleasures was to amuse those about him. What would he not do to raise my spirits when I was sad or ill?

It was easy to feel the honesty of his characteristics. From his father he had received his tendency to experiment, that minute observation of things which caused him to spend infinite time in accounting to himself for the smallest detail, and that taste for all knowledge which made him a scholar as well as an artist. His mother transmitted to him his impressionability and that almost feminine tenderness which often made his great heart overflow and his eyes grow moist at the sight of a child. His taste for travel, he often said, came to him from one of his ancestors who took part in the conquest of Canada. He was very proud of counting up the brave ones among his own people, any one who had brains and was not *bourgeois;* for he had a hatred of the *bourgeois,* and continually employed that term as a synonym for mediocrity and envy, the living only with the appearance of virtue and insulting all grandeur and beauty.

At the death of Laumonier, my grandfather succeeded him as surgeon-in-chief of the Hospital. It was in this vast building that Gustave Flaubert was born.

The Hospital at Rouen, of the construction of the last century, is not wanting in a certain kind of character; the straight lines of its architecture present something of chasteness and something of the accepted modern types. It was situated at the end of Rue de Crosne, and as one came from the centre of the town he found himself face to face with the great arch of the iron gate, all black, behind which was a court-yard with willows planted in rows: at the end and built around the sides was the edifice.

The part occupied by my grandparents formed a wing, approached by a private entrance. At the left of the central gate, a high door opened upon a court where grass grew among the old paving stones. On the other side of the pavilion was a garden forming an angle with the street, bordered at the left by a wall covered with ivy and hemmed in at the right by the hospital buildings. These are high grey walls, punctured with little glazed holes to which meagre faces are glued, their heads bound in white linen cloths. These ghastly silhouettes with hollow eyes show great suffering and have a profound sadness about them.

Gustave's room was on the side of the entrance, in the second story. The view was upon the hospital gardens overlooking the trees, under whose verdure the patients sat on stone seats, when the weather was pleasant. From time to time the white wing of a great bonnet of one of the sisters could be seen rapidly crossing the courtyard, and sometimes there were visitors, the parents of the invalids, or the friends of the attendants, but never any noise or anything unexpected.

This severe and melancholy place could not have been without influence upon Gustave Flaubert. He ever retained an exquisite compassion for all human

1

suffering, and also a high morality, which would scarcely be suspected by those who are scandalised by his paradoxes.

No one was less like what is usually called an artist than my uncle. Among the peculiarities of his character, the contrasts have always astonished me. This man, so preoccupied with beauty in style and giving form so high a place, even the highest, paid little attention to the beauty that surrounded him; his own furniture was of heavy contour, not the least delicate, and he had no taste for objects of art (bric-à-brac) so much in vogue at that time.

He loved order with a passion, carrying it to a mania, and would never work until his books were arranged in a certain fashion. He preserved carefully all letters addressed to him. I have large boxes full of them. Did he think there would be as much interest taken in them as there was later in his own? Did he foresee that great interest in his correspondence (which reveals the man in a light so different from that revealed by his works), that he imposed upon me the task of collecting and publishing it? No one can say.

He always observed extreme regularity in his work each day. He yoked himself to it as an ox is yoked to a cart, without waiting for that inspiration which expectation renders fruitless, as he said. His energy of will for all that concerned his art was prodigious, and his patience was tireless. Some years before his death, he would amuse himself by saying: "I am the last of the Fathers of the Church," and, in fact, with his long, maroon-coloured wrapper and a little black silk cap on the top of his head, he was something like a recluse of Port-Royal.

I can see him now running over the terrace at Croisset, absorbed in thought, stopping suddenly, his arms crossed, raising his head and remaining for some moments with his eyes fixed on the space above, and then resuming his walk again.

Life at the Hospital was regular, free, and good. My grandfather, who had attained a high reputation, medically, gave his children all that ease and tenderness could add to the happiness of youth. He had bought a house in the country, at Deville near Rouen, which he disposed of one year before his death, a railroad having cut through the garden only a few metres from the house. It was then that he bought Croisset, on the banks of the Seine.

Each year the entire family went to Nogent-on-the Seine to the home of the Flaubert parents. It was quite a journey, which we made in a post-chaise, a veritable journey of the good old times. The thought of them brought many an amusing remembrance to my uncle; but those which were most charming to him were his vacations passed at Trouville, then but a simple fishing village.

He met there some English people, the family of Admiral Collier, all of whom were beautiful and intelligent. The oldest daughters, Gertrude and Henrietta, soon became the intimate friends of my uncle and my mother. Gertrude, now Madame Tennant, lately wrote me some pages about her youth. I translate the following lines:—

"Gustave Flaubert was then like a young Greek. In full adolescence, he was tall and thin, supple and graceful as an athlete, unconscious of the gifts that he possessed, physically and morally, caring little for the impression he produced and entirely indifferent to accepted form. His dress consisted of a red flannel shirt, great trousers of blue cloth, a scarf of the same color around his waist and a cap put on no matter how, or often bare-headed. When I spoke to him of fame, or of influence, as desirable things that I esteemed, he listened, smiled, and seemed superbly indifferent. He admired what was beautiful in nature, art and literature and lived for that, as he said, without any thought of the personal. He cared neither for glory nor for gain. Was it not enough that a thing was true and beautiful? His great joy was in finding something that he judged worthy of admiration. The charm of his society was in his enthusiasm for all that was noble; and the charm of his mind was its intense individuality. He hated all hypocrisy. What was lacking in his nature, was an interest in exterior and useful things. If any one happened to say that religion, politics, or business had as great an interest for them as literature or art, he would open his eyes in astonishment and pity. To be literary, an artist, that alone was worth living for."

It was at Trouville also that he met the musical editor, Maurice Schlesinger and his wife. Many faces remained engraved on his memory of his sojourns by the sea, among others that of an old sailor, Captain Barbet and his little daughter, Barbette, a little humpback always crying out to her dolls. Then there was Doctor Billard, and Father Couillère, mayor of the commune, at whose house they had repasts that lasted for six hours. He recalled these years in writing *A Simple Soul*. Madame Aubin, her two children, the house where she lived, and all the details so true, so appreciative, in this simple history, are of striking exactness. Madame was an aunt to my grandmother; Félicité and her parrot once lived.

In his last years, my uncle had an extreme desire to revive his youth. He wrote *A Simple Soul*, after his mother's death, to try to accomplish this. In painting the town where she was born, the hearth before which she had played, his cousins, the companions of his childhood, he found satisfaction, and that pleasure has brought from his pen his most touching pages, those perhaps where he allows us to divine most clearly the man under the writer. Recall that scene where Madame Aubin and her servant are arranging the trifling possessions that had belonged to Virginia. A large hat of black straw which my grandmother had worn awoke in my uncle a similar emotion. He would take that relic from the nail, look at it in silence, with eyes moistening, and then respectfully replace it.

Finally, the happy time of leaving college arrived, but the terrible question of choosing a profession, or taking up some career poisoned his joy. As a vocation, he cared only for literature, and "literature" is not a career; it leads to no "position." My grandfather wished his son to be a savant and a law practitioner. To devote himself to the unique and exclusive research for beauty of literary form, seemed to him almost folly. A man of character, eminently strong, and of very active habits, he comprehended with difficulty the nervous and somewhat feminine side which characterises all artistic organisations. With his mother my uncle found more encouragement, but she held to the point that he should obey his father, and he was resolved that Gustave should make his way in Paris. He set out, sad at leaving his own people, his sister especially.

At Paris he lived in the Rue de l'Est in a little bachelor apartment where he found himself badly installed. The noisy, free and easy pleasures of his comrades seemed to him stupid, so that he scarcely ever participated in them. He would remain alone, open one of his law books, which he would immediately put away, then extending himself upon his bed, he would smoke and dream for hours. He became very weary of this life, and grew sombre.

Pradier's studio alone put warmth in him again; he saw there all the artists of the day, and in contact with them he felt his instincts grow. One day he met Victor Hugo there. Some women visited the studio; it was there he met Louise Colet. He often went to see the pretty English girls of Trouville, to the salon of the editor, Maurice Schlesinger, and to the hospitable house of his father's friend, Doctor Jules Cloquet, who led him away one summer to the Pyrenees and to Corsica. The *Education Sentimental* was composed in remembrance of this epoch.

But in spite of friendship,—doubtless in spite of love,—a weariness without bounds invaded him. His work, which was contrary to his taste, became intolerable to him, his health was seriously affected and he returned to Rouen.

My mother's marriage, her death the year following, and a little later that of my grandfather, left my grandmother in such grief that she was happy to keep her son near her. Paris and the Law School were abandoned. It was then that, in company with Maxime Ducamp, he made the journey through Brittany and they wrote together the book: *Over Strand and Field. (A travers les Champs et les Grèves.)*

Upon his return, he began his *Saint Antoine,* his first great work. It had been preceded by many, of which fragments have been published since his death. The *Saint Antoine* composed then, was not the first known to the public. This work was undertaken at three different times before it was finally finished.

In 1849 Gustave Flaubert took a second journey with Maxime Ducamp. This time the two friends directed their steps towards the Orient, which had for so long been their dream!

II.

My personal reminiscences date from his return. He came back at evening; I was in bed, but they awakened me. He came to my little bed, raised me suddenly and found me very droll in my long nightgown; I remember that it extended far below my feet. He began to laugh very hard and then to imprint great kisses on my cheeks which made me cry; I felt the cold of his moustache, humid with dew, and was very glad when he put me down again. I was then five years old and we were at the grandparents' house at Nogent. Three months later I saw him again in England, as I still remember distinctly. It was at the time of the first Exposition at London. They took me there and the crowd frightened me; my uncle took me on his shoulder, and I traversed the galleries overlooking everybody, this time happy to be in his arms. They chose me a governess and we returned to Croisset.

My uncle wished to begin my education immediately. The governess was to teach me only English; my grandmother would teach me to read and write, and for him was reserved history and geography. He believed it useless to study grammar, holding that it taught itself in reading, and that it was bad to charge the memory of a young child with abstractions, which one begins where often they ought to finish.

Then began some years when we were all together.

Croisset, where we lived, is the first village on the bank of the Seine in going from Rouen to Havre. The house, long and low in shape, all white, must have been built about two hundred years. It had belonged to the monks of the Abbey of Saint-Ouen whom it served for a country house, and it pleased my uncle to think that Prévost had composed *Manon Lescaut* here.

In the interior court, where still remained the pointed roof and the guillotine-shaped windows of the seventeenth century, the construction was interesting, but the façade was ugly. It had undergone one of those remodellings in bad taste that were seen so often in the first Empire and the reign of Louis Philippe, at the beginning of the century. Above the entrance, after the fashion of bas-reliefs, were some villainous casts,—the seasons of Bouchardon—and the mantelpiece in the salon had on each side a representation of a mummy in white marble, a souvenir of the Egyptian country.

The rooms were few, but sufficiently large. The spacious dining-room, which occupied the centre of the house on the ground floor, opened upon the garden by a glass door flanked by two windows in full view of the river. It was pleasing and gay.

On the next story, at the right, a long corridor separated the chambers, and on the left was my uncle's study, or work-room. It was a large apartment, with a very low ceiling, but very light, because of five windows, of which three looked upon